THE PLEASURES OF MATH

THE
PLEASURES
OF
MATH

by A. W. Goodman

The University of South Florida
Tampa, Florida

THE MACMILLAN COMPANY, NEW YORK
COLLIER-MACMILLAN LTD., LONDON

Library of Congress Catalog Card Number: 63–7176
First Printing 1965

The Macmillan Company, New York
Collier-Macmillan Canada Ltd., Toronto, Ontario
Divisions of The Crowell-Collier Publishing Company

Printed in the United States of America

CONTENTS

6 / Contents

PREFACE

With the launching of the first Sputnik by the Russians, the American people realized that a society which was regarded as less advanced than ours, was in fact, definitely ahead of ours in at least one field. And of course there was the uneasy feeling that perhaps the Russians were also ahead in many other branches of science and technology. This feeling was later strengthened by the Soviet success in sending men into orbit around the earth.

What can we do? No amount of money and advertising can overnight produce leading scientists. The training must start early and be conducted in an atmosphere that recognizes, appreciates, respects, and rewards the budding scientist.

As proof that we have failed to provide this type of atmosphere, we need only look at the roster of those men who were mainly responsible for the development of our major defensive weapon, the atom bomb. Here is a partial list[1] together with the country in which they received their early training: Hans Bethe (Germany), Niels Bohr (Denmark), Edward Condon (United States), Enrico Fermi (Italy), Klaus Fuchs (Germany), George Gamow (Russia), Ernest Lawrence (United States), Robert Oppenheimer (United States), Louis Slotin (Canada), Leo Szilard (Hun-

[1] A very readable and interesting account of these men and their contributions to creating the atom and hydrogen bombs can be found in Robert Jungk, *Brighter Than a Thousand Suns* (New York: Harcourt, Brace and Co., 1958).

gary), Edward Teller (Hungary), Stan Ulam (Poland), Victor Weisskopf (Austria), and Eugene Wigner (Hungary).

We can be very thankful that it was the remarkable political institutions set up by the founders of this government that attracted so many outstanding scientists to our country.

But we can not continue to rely forever on foreign countries for our supply of scientists. A first step toward improving the education of our own potential scientists, is to enlarge the content of the mathematics courses in our grade schools and our high schools.

At present a vast majority of students entering college know a lot of arithmetic, a little manipulative algebra, some Euclidean geometry, and a little trigonometry. But they are totally unaware of the existence of a vast amount of mathematics that is fascinating, challenging, stimulating, and, moreover, quite beautiful. The damage inflicted by our present diluted and turtle-paced courses is augmented because the student's mind is allowed to remain dormant during just that period when it should be experiencing maximum growth. It is too much to expect that it can be suddenly awakened in college to do the difficult work expected of a college student.

It is the author's intent in this book to help change the present sad situation by providing an inkling of some of the exciting things awaiting the delver into the wonderful world of mathematics. It is aimed at four classes of readers. First, it is directed to the high school student who intends to be a scientist (the particular field is of no importance) and who wants to know more about mathematics than his present courses provide. Second, it can be used by those sincere high school teachers who want to know more about mathematics so that they can do a better job of teaching. It is also designed for college students who want to know more mathematics than their standard courses offer. Finally, it can be read by parents who have had a little mathematics, but who wish to widen their horizons, so that they can encourage and stimulate the intellectual growth of their children. This last group is far more important than is generally realized, because it is the parents who provide the main influence on the child during his early development.

A number of topics that should be taught in the high schools, but which frequently have been diluted or dropped, are restored to their rightful place in this book. These are (a) mathematical induction, (b) inequalities, (c) conic sections, and (d) permutations and combinations. For diversity, breadth, and amusement, I have included material on (a) magic squares, (b) the four color problem, (c) extreme values without using the calculus, (d) prime numbers, and (e) mathematical intuition.

I do not try to introduce calculus in this book, because I feel that calculus is strictly a college course. However a student who finishes this book working most of the exercises is fully prepared to start on calculus. If he finds that such a course is not available (he may still be in high school) he should purchase a calculus book and start in on his own. There is no point in wasting time.

In writing this book I have tried to explain every step in complete detail, so that this book can be used by anyone who has a slight knowledge of elementary algebra and plane geometry. No trigonometry is used in this book. To assist the reader, the answers to all of the numerical problems are given in the back of this book, and further hints on the solutions of the logical problems are included. Difficult sections or problems are marked with a star (★) and the more difficult ones with a double star (★★), so the reader can be on guard. The chapters are designed to be studied in sequence but the reader need not take them in order, nor cover them all. The schematic drawing on page 12 shows the interdependence of the chapters. For example the arrow drawn from Chapter 1 to Chapter 10 indicates that Chapter 1 should be studied prior to Chapter 10, but that none of the other chapters are needed for the material of Chapter 10. Those chapters at the end of the line, such as Chapters 3, 6, 10, 11 and 12, can be skipped if time is short, but these chapters contain much that is interesting, and the student who fails to read them is missing something in his mathematical life.

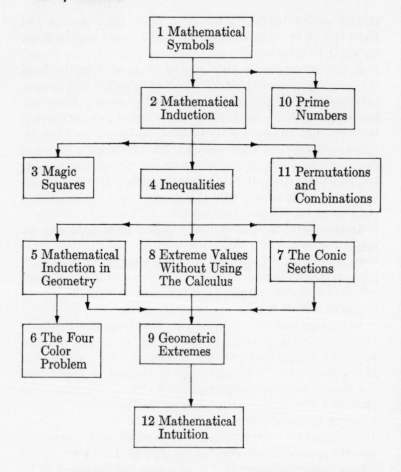

Although mathematics as a tool is indispensable to any scientist, is this the only reason to study mathematics? If the governments of Russia and China were suddenly to become devoted to peace, would the need to study mathematics also vanish? Indeed, why should you study mathematics?[2]

Instead of answering this specific question, let us shift the subject matter and ask a parallel question. Why

[2]This portion of the Preface, and the first six sections of Chapter 1, are reprinted with permission from the author's *Plane Trigonometry* (New York: John Wiley and Sons, Inc., 1959).

should you do anything at all in life? Why should you learn to swim? Why should you learn to play a musical instrument? Why should you learn to bowl or play chess? Basically the answer is the same in all cases. You do these things because they are fun. Or if they aren't fun at first you hope that as you acquire proficiency they will become fun. Only a few professionals make money from playing basketball or swimming, or playing the piano, but nearly everyone enjoys at least one of these activities, and some fortunate individuals enjoy all three. If exercising your muscles by playing tennis or pole-vaulting can give pleasure, there is no reason why you can't also enjoy exercising your brain by doing mathematics.

Mathematics is the greatest game ever invented by man.

Learn to play the game a little bit, and see if you don't enjoy it.

CHAPTER I

Mathematical Symbols

1. A five-minute history of mathematical symbols. In the early days of mathematical study, ideas were expressed by long complicated sentences in the language then in vogue (Greek, Arabic, Latin, etc.). Little by little the early geniuses realized that the sentences could be shortened if some symbols were used for words and often they merely chose the first letter of the key word. If such a system were in use today, "solve the equation $x^4 - 3\,x^2 + 2 = 0$ for x" might read:

Find u so that: ututumthtutuptweqz.

Here u represents the unknown, t stands for times, and p and m stand for plus and minus, respectively. The letter pairs, *th* for three and *tw* for two, would be used to avoid confusion with t for times. Clearly z would mean zero, and *eq* would mean equals.

Although such a system is bad, it is not completely impossible. Indeed, despite the handicaps imposed by poor notation, the early mathematicians made remarkable discoveries. What made matters worse was the fact that communication was slow, and libraries rare, so that for the most part each society developed its own system of symbols. Thus today when an archeologist unearths a manuscript, a mere knowledge of mathematics and the language of the manuscript may not be sufficient for reading the treasure. He would also need to know the symbols used by the writer before he could distinguish a valuable mathematical document from an account of a military expedition or the records of some collector of taxes.

The symbols we now use were introduced little by little

14

and all of them within the past five hundred years. Table I gives more detailed information. Once introduced the symbols did not become popular overnight. On the contrary, often fifty years or more elapsed before anything resembling a unanimous adoption of the symbol was achieved.

TABLE I

Symbol	Meaning or Name	Date Introduced	Inventor
$+$	Plus	1486	Unknown
$-$	Minus	1486	Unknown
$\sqrt{\ }$	Square Root	1526	Christoff Rudolff
$(\ )$	Parentheses	1556	Nicolo Fontana Tartaglia
$=$	Equals	1557	Robert Recorde
.	Decimal Point	1617	John Napier
$>$	Greater than	1631	Thomas Harriot
$<$	Less than	1631	Thomas Harriot
$\times$	Multiplication	1631	William Oughtred
$\cdot$	Multiplication	1631	Thomas Harriot
AB	Multiplication by juxtaposition	1637	René Descartes
x,y,z	Letters near the end of the alphabet for unknown quantities	1637	René Descartes
a,b,c	letters near the beginning of the alphabet for known quantities	1637	René Descartes
$\div$	Division	1659	Johann Rahn
$\leqq$	Less than or equal to	1734	Pierre Bouguer
$\geqq$	Greater than or equal to	1734	Pierre Bouguer
$\neq$	not equal	1740(?)	Leonhard Euler(?)
a^n	The exponent notation		See below
$a^1, a^2, a^3, \cdots$	n a positive integer	1637	René Descartes
$a^{-1}, a^{1/2}, \cdots$	n a negative integer or a fraction	1659	John Wallis
a^n	n any real number	1676	Isaac Newton
π	The ratio of circumference to diameter in a circle	1706	William Jones

Today mathematicians are in a much more fortunate position. All of the symbols[1] in the table and a great many other symbols used in higher mathematics are used throughout the civilized world, always with the same meaning. As a result, new mathematical discoveries made and published in one part of the world can be immediately read and understood by mathematicians everywhere.

The reader who wants more details on the history and the early development of mathematics would do well to consult one or more of the following books:

Howard Eves, *An Introduction to the History of Mathematics* (New York: Rinehart and Co., 1953).

Vera Sanford, *A Short History of Mathematics* (New York: Houghton Mifflin Co., 1930).

Florian Cajori, *A History of Mathematics*, 2nd ed. (New York: The Macmillan Co., 1919).

W. W. R. Ball, *History of Mathematics* (New York: The Macmillan Co., 1908).

2. Subscripts. Suppose that we have a problem involving the radii of four circles (the exact nature of the problem is unimportant). It is natural to use the letter r for the radius of one of the circles, and R for the radius of the second circle, since both r and R tend to remind us of the word radius. For the radius of the third circle, we might choose the Greek letter ρ (rho) which corresponds to the English r. But now we are stuck for a suitable choice of symbol for the radius of the fourth circle. The way out is quite simple. We return to the letter r and put little numbers (called subscripts) just below the letter, thus: r_1, r_2, r_3, r_4, and use these to represent the radii of the four circles. These symbols are read: r sub-one, r sub-two, etc. If we are in a hurry we may just say: r-one, r-two, etc. In the symbol r_2, the number 2 is written below the line (subscript) in order to distinguish it from $r2$, which would be interpreted as the product of r and 2.

3. One symbol with several meanings. Mathematics

---

[1] There is one exception to this statement. In many countries the comma is used for the decimal point instead of the period.

is sometimes called, "the language of science." In any complicated language it frequently happens that one word may have a variety of meanings. For example in English the word "bridge" may mean (1) a structure carrying a roadway for autos, erected over a river, (2) the upper bony part of the nose, (3) the part of a pair of glasses that rests on the nose, (4) a device for securing artificial teeth, (5) a support for a cue stick in the game of billiards, (6) a portion of an electric circuit, or (7) a card game. The rich variety of meanings for the word "bridge" does not cause any difficulty and no one complains about the English language because it has a large number of words each with a multitude of meanings. In any given sentence the meaning of the word "bridge" is clear from the way in which it is used in the sentence.

Similarly, in mathematics a symbol can be used with several different meanings. For example, what does the letter A represent in Figure 1.1? Actually, it can denote the point which is the intersection of two lines, or it can

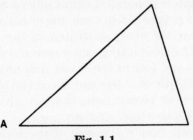

A

Fig. 1.1

represent the angle formed by the two lines, or it can denote the measure of the angle, in this case 40°. Each of these three items (the point, the angle, and the measure of the angle) is logically distinct and it may seem to be improper to use one letter A for all three. But how much more confusing it would be to use three different letters at each corner of the triangle. It is better to use just one letter A. An alert student will have no trouble in discerning from the context just which of the items the letter represents at a given time, just as he can determine the meaning of the word "bridge" from the way it is used.

4. What is a theorem? A rough definition is this: a theorem is a statement or assertion that can be proved. We will not try to polish this definition, but we want to indicate what the rough spots are. The statement "George Washington was the first president of the United States" can be "proved" by consulting several history books. However we do not call this statement a theorem, (1) because it does not deal with a mathematical object and (2) because the proof is not given by a logical argument. In this case the proof given is "proof by appeal to higher authority" and such proofs by appeal are never allowed in mathematics.

The assertion "$2 + 2 = 4$" is a valid statement, and it can be proved by a logical argument, beginning with the three definitions $1 + 1 = 2$, $1 + 2 = 3$, and $1 + 3 = 4$ and using the associative law of addition. Still we do not wish to call $2 + 2 = 4$ a theorem, because it is not very interesting, and also it is not very important for the development of mathematics.

Mathematics is populated with millions of facts, formulas, laws, and propositions, each one provable by a logical argument. To call every such item a theorem would be ridiculous. The fascinating and important facts would be swallowed up and lost in the sea of dull and trivial items. The honorable title of "theorem" is reserved for those facts, formulas, laws, or propositions that are either very interesting or very important, or both.

Although one man's theorem may be another man's proposition, this should not confuse the student. The important thing to remember is this: whether it is a mathematical proposition, or theorem, it can be proved by logical arguments.

One should not demand a proof of every assertion, because this is logically impossible. Certain of the simplest assertions are needed as "building blocks" with which to give the proofs of the more complicated ones. Since every proof needs some building blocks it is clear that in order to begin somewhere, some of the assertions must be assumed valid without proof. Such assertions are called *axioms* or *postulates*. For example, in plane geometry the assertion "Through any pair of points one and only one line can be drawn" is an axiom. Any attempt to prove it would only result in introducing other and more complicated axioms.

5. The notation Q.E.D. We put the symbols Q.E.D. at the end of a proof. These letters abbreviate the Latin phrase *quod erat demonstrandum* which means "which was to be demonstrated." These letters serve to notify the student that the proof of the theorem has been completed. He may not understand the proof, but at least he can locate the point at which the proof stops, and then reread the proof until it does become clear.

★6. Function notation.[2] Just as we use x to represent a number in mathematics, we need some notation for a function. A function is a correspondence between two sets of numbers, such that when one number from the first set is given, its mate in the second set can be determined. Thus y is called a function of x if whenever x is known y can be found. As examples of functions we cite:

$$(1) \qquad y = 5x + 3,$$
$$(2) \qquad y = x^3 - 2x^2 + 3x - 4,$$
$$(3) \qquad y = 2^x,$$
$$(4) \qquad y = \frac{x^5 + 3x^3 - 22}{x^2 + \pi}.$$

In each of these examples, whenever x is a given number we can compute y. We call x the *independent variable*, because it can run freely and y is called the *dependent variable*, because the value of y depends on the value of x.

In these examples, the functions are explicitly known. When we wish to talk about an unknown function, or just talk about functions in general, we use the symbol

$$y = f(x)$$

(read "y equals f of x").

[2]The notation explained in this section is not used again until Chapter 5. The reader can postpone reading this until later, if it appears to be too difficult. In that case he should also skip problems 3 through 8 of the next exercise list.

Here the f does not multiply x, but it is a machine or an operator that produces from each x its mate y. For example, if $x = 2$ and if $f(x)$ is the particular function given by equation (1), then

$$f(2) = 5 \times 2 + 3 = 13.$$

Briefly: to find $f(2)$, knowing $f(x)$, just replace x by 2 wherever x occurs. For this same function we have

$$f(1) = 5 \times 1 + 3 = 8,$$

and

$$f(3) = 5 \times 3 + 3 = 18.$$

Notice that

$$f(1) + f(2) = 8 + 13 = 21,$$

but

$$f(1 + 2) = f(3) = 18.$$

Therefore we observe that

$$f(1 + 2) \neq f(1) + f(2),$$

where the symbol $\neq$ means "not equal."

Example. If $f(x) = 2x - 7$ prove that

(5) $$f(3x) = 3f(x) + 14.$$

Solution. For the left side of equation (5) we have:

$$f(3x) = 2(3x) - 7 = 6x - 7.$$

For the right side of equation (5) we have:

$$3f(x) + 14 = 3(2x - 7) + 14$$
$$= 6x - 21 + 14$$
$$= 6x - 7.$$

Since each side of (5) is equal to $6x - 7$, the two sides are equal. Q.E.D.

7. The "three dots" notation. Suppose we wish to add the integers from 1 to 10. It is a little tiresome to write them down thus:

$$1 + 2 + 3 + 4 + 5 + 6 + 7 + 8 + 9 + 10,$$

but still we can do it, and then find the sum. But if we are asked to write the integers from 1 to 100 and add them, we would regard the task as a burden. If we are asked to write the integers from 1 to 1,000,000 and add them we would certainly refuse, because writing at the rate of one number per second it would take about 11 days just to write the numbers. And yet in mathematics we frequently wish to consider problems involving sums of series such as these. In order to remove some of the burdensome tasks from mathematics, and leave only the pleasant ones, the "three dots" notation has been introduced. Thus the first sum would be written

$$1 + 2 + 3 + \cdots + 10,$$

the second one would be written

$$1 + 2 + 3 + \cdots + 100,$$

and for the third one we would write

$$1 + 2 + 3 + \cdots + 1,000,000.$$

As the examples show, we write down the first few terms of the series, just enough to show the general law of formation. Then we follow with "three dots" to indicate that the series continues in the obvious way, and finally we indicate the stopping place. The three dots represent the missing terms, and these terms must be considered as present even though we did not explicitly write them.

In fact if we want to make the last integer a variable n, instead of the specific integer 1,000,000, we can merely write

$$1 + 2 + 3 + \cdots + n.$$

Without the three dots or some other symbol to represent the missing terms it would be impossible to indicate such a sum.

We will see in Chapter 2 that the sum of the first n positive integers is given by the formula

$$(6) \qquad 1 + 2 + 3 + \cdots + n = \frac{n(n + 1)}{2}.$$

Using the formula we can immediately write that the sum

of the integers from 1 to 1,000,000 is

$$\frac{1,000,000 \times 1,000,001}{2} = 500,000,500,000.$$

Is it not remarkable that we can obtain the sum of a string of numbers so long, that we have not the time, nor the energy to write them all down?

★8. **The absolute value notation.** It is convenient to have a notation which tells us to "throw away" the negative sign when x is negative. The symbol for this is $|x|$ (read "absolute value of x" or "numerical value of x"). For example $|3| = 3$, while $|-3| = 3$. Unfortunately, if we just look at the symbol x there is no way of telling whether it represents a positive number or a negative one. Therefore in a formal definition the phrase "throw away the negative sign" can not be used. If we recall that $-(-3) = +3$, then the way out of our difficulty is easy.

Definition 1. *If x is any number, then $|x|$ is defined as follows:*

$|x| = x,$ *if* $x \geqq 0,$ *(if x is positive or zero)*
$|x| = -x,$ *if* $x < 0,$ *(if x is negative).*

According to this definition $|13| = 13$, $|0| = 0$, and $|-7| = -(-7) = 7$.

Exercise 1

★1. Give all possible interpretations for the expression

$$\frac{\dfrac{A}{B}}{\dfrac{C}{D}}$$

and simplify this expression for each interpretation. There are five interpretations, but only four different answers.

★2. If A, B, and C are all different from zero, when is

$$\frac{\dfrac{A}{B}}{C} = \frac{A}{\dfrac{B}{C}}?$$

3. If $f(x) = x^3 - 2x^2 + 3x - 4$, show that $f(1) = -2$, $f(2) = 2$, $f(3) = 14$, $f(0) = -4$, and $f(-2) = -26$.

4. If $f(x) = 2^x$, show that $f(1) = 2$, $f(5) = 32$, $f(0) = 1$, and $f(-1) = \frac{1}{2}$.

★**5.** For the function $f(x) = 11x$ prove that $f(x+y) = f(x) + f(y)$.

★**6.** For the function $f(x) = x^2$ prove that $f(x) = f(-x)$ and that $f(x+6) = x^2 + 12x + 36$.

★**7.** For the function $f(x) = x^7$ prove that $f(-x) = -f(x)$ and that $f(xy) = x^7y^7 = f(x)\,f(y)$.

★**8.** For the function $f(x) = 5^x$ prove that $f(x+y) = (x)f(y)$.

9. Write those terms which are represented by the three dots in

$(a)\ 1 + 3 + 5 + \cdots + 17,$
$(b)\ 1 + 4 + 9 + \cdots + 49,$
$(c)\ -2 + 4 - 8 + 16 - \cdots + 256.$

10. Use equation (6) to compute the sum of the positive integers from 1 to 500 inclusive.

★**11.** Use equation (6) to compute the sum of the positive integers from 5 to 400 inclusive.

12. Find the sum of all of the even integers from 2 to 1000 inclusive. *Hint:* Double the answer to problem 10.

★**13.** Find the sum of all of the odd integers from 1 to 999.

★**14.** Find $(a)\ |\sqrt{15} - 4|$, $\quad(b)\ |\sqrt[3]{11} - \sqrt{5}|$, $(c)\ |x^2 - 2xy + y^2|$.

★**15.** Prove that for any numbers x and y,

$$|xy| = |x| \cdot |y|.$$

Hint: Consider various possible cases.

★**16.** Prove that for any numbers x and y,

$$|x+y| \leqq |x| + |y|.$$

★**17.** Prove that for any numbers x and y,

$$|x-y| \geqq |x| - |y|.$$

CHAPTER 2

Mathematical Induction

1. An example. Let us try to add together the first n odd positive integers, where n is any integer. By direct computation we find that:

if $n = 1$	$1 = 1$	$= 1^2$,
if $n = 2$	$1 + 3 = 4$	$= 2^2$,
if $n = 3$	$1 + 3 + 5 = 9$	$= 3^2$,
if $n = 4$	$1 + 3 + 5 + 7 = 16$	$= 4^2$,
if $n = 5$	$1 + 3 + 5 + 7 + 9 = 25$	$= 5^2$,
if $n = 6$	$1 + 3 + 5 + 7 + 9 + 11 = 36$	$= 6^2$.

An examination of these cases leads us to believe that the sum is always the square of the number of terms in the sum. To express this symbolically we should observe that if n is the number of terms, it seems as though $2n - 1$ is the last term in the sum. To check this we notice that:

if $n = 1$	$2n - 1 = 2 - 1 = 1$,
if $n = 2$	$2n - 1 = 4 - 1 = 3$,
if $n = 3$	$2n - 1 = 6 - 1 = 5$,
if $n = 4$	$2n - 1 = 8 - 1 = 7$,

and so on. Thus we can express our assertion for general n by the equation

$$(1) \qquad 1 + 3 + 5 + 7 + \cdots + (2n - 1) = n^2,$$

because the nth odd integer is $2n - 1$.

2. Some counter-examples. We have already seen by

24

direct calculation that equation (1) holds whe
any one of the values 1, 3, 5, 7, 9, and 11. D
that equation (1) is valid for any positiv
$2n - 1$? Can we settle this by continuing
work? We might try the case when $2n - $
$n = 12$. Direct computation shows that:

$$1 + 3 + 5 + 7 + 9 + 11 + 13 + 15 + 17$$
$$+ 19 + 21 + 23 = 144 = 12^2,$$

so that again our formula (1) seems to hold. One might be
tempted to say that since the terminal odd number 23 was
selected at random this proves that (1) is valid for every
possible choice of the terminal number. Actually, no matter how many cases we check, we can never prove that (1)
is always valid, because there are infinitely many cases, and
no amount of pure computation can settle them all. What
is needed is some *logical* argument that will *prove* that
equation (1) is always valid.

Before we give the details of this logical argument, we
will give some examples of assertions which can be checked
experimentally for small values of n, but which after careful investigation turn out to be false for certain other
values of n.

Let us first examine the numbers A of the form

(2) $$A = 2^{2^n} + 1.$$

We find by direct computation that:

if $n = 0$,	$2^n = 2^0 = 1$,	$A = 2^1 + 1 = 3$,
if $n = 1$,	$2^n = 2^1 = 2$,	$A = 2^2 + 1 = 5$,
if $n = 2$,	$2^n = 2^2 = 4$,	$A = 2^4 + 1 = 17$,
if $n = 3$,	$2^n = 2^3 = 8$,	$A = 2^8 + 1 = 257$,
if $n = 4$,	$2^n = 2^4 = 16$,	$A = 2^{16} + 1 = 65{,}537$.

Each of these values for A is a prime, *i.e.* an integer (whole
number) which has no divisor other than itself and one
(with the quotient also an integer). Can we assert on the
basis of these five examples, that A is always prime for
every positive integer n? Of course not. We might conjecture that this is true but we should not make a positive
assertion, unless we can supply a proof valid for all n. In

.act Fermat (1601–1665), the great French mathematician, did conjecture exactly that, but about a hundred years later Euler (1707–1783), the great Swiss mathematician, showed that for $n = 5$

$$A = 2^{2^5} + 1 = 4,294,967,297 = 641 \times 6,700,417$$

and hence A is not a prime for $n = 5$.

The German mathematician Leibniz (1646–1716), one of the creators of the calculus, proved that for each positive integer n:

$$n^3 - n \text{ is divisible by 3,}$$
$$n^5 - n \text{ is divisible by 5,}$$
$$n^7 - n \text{ is divisible by 7,}$$

and he conjectured that for any positive odd integer k

$$n^k - n \text{ is divisible by } k.$$

But he exploded his own conjecture by showing that

$$2^9 - 2 = 510$$

and this number is not divisible by 9.

Next consider the inequality[1]

(3) $$2^n < n^{10} + 2.$$

If we put in values for n we find that:

if $n = 1$ we have $2 < 1 + 2 = 3$,
if $n = 2$ we have $4 < 1024 + 2 = 1026$,
if $n = 3$ we have $8 < 59,051$,
if $n = 4$ we have $16 < 1,048,578$.

It certainly looks as though the inequality (3) is valid for every positive integer n. If we try a large value of n, say $n = 20$, then the inequality (3) asserts that

$$1,048,576 < 10,240,000,000,002,$$

which is certainly true. But even this computation does not prove that (3) is always valid, and in fact such an as-

---

[1]See Chapter 4 for a detailed discussion of inequalities. The symbol $a < b$ means a is less than b.

sertion is *false*. For if we set $n = 59$ we find that (approximately)

$$2^{59} = 5.764 \times 10^{17} \quad \text{and} \quad 59^{10} + 2 = 5.111 \times 10^{17}$$

and now the first term in (3) is *larger* than the second. In fact it is not hard to prove that for every n larger than 59 *the inequality (3) is false*.

We give one more example, which, although trivial, still illustrates our central point. We make the assertion that
    "*Every positive integer n is less than 1,000,001.*"

This is obviously false, and yet if we begin by setting first $n = 1$, then $n = 2$, then $n = 3, \cdots$, it is clear that for the first million cases that we check, the assertion is true. The falsity is not revealed until we set $n = 1,000,001$. Although this example may seem artificial, it is not difficult to give quite natural examples of the same phenomenon, although such examples would necessarily be more complicated.

We can not conclude that an assertion involving an integer n is true for all positive values of the integer n, merely by checking specific values of n, no matter how many we check.

3. The general principle. Let us use the symbol $P(n)$ (read "P of n") to denote some proposition which depends on n. For example $P(n)$ might denote the proposition that

(1) $1 + 3 + 5 + 7 + \cdots + (2n - 1) = n^2.$

Suppose that $P(n)$ is not always true, *i.e.* suppose there is some integer n for which the proposition is false. Then obviously there is some smallest integer with the same property, *i.e.* if we denote this smallest integer by $k + 1$, then there is an integer k such that $P(k)$ is true and $P(k + 1)$ is false. If we want to prove that this cannot occur then we must prove that: whenever the proposition is true for the integer k then it is also true for the integer $k + 1$. If we have proved this, then it cannot happen that $P(k)$ is true and at the same time $P(k + 1)$ is false.

Finally among the set of all positive integers k, 1 is the smallest. The proposition might be meaningless for $k = 0$, and hence this exceptional case would not be covered by the preceding argument. Thus to prove that $P(n)$ is true for all positive integers, we must also prove it when $n = 1$.

Thus the proof that $P(n)$ is valid for all positive integers can be given in two steps, and these two steps together form the:

Principle of Mathematical Induction. *If for a given assertion $P(n)$ we can prove that:*

1°. *The assertion is true for $n = 1$.*
2°. *If it is true for index $n = k$, then it is also true for index $n = k + 1$.*

Then the assertion is true for every positive integer n.

We have already proved this principle in our preceding discussion. We now illustrate the use of this principle by proving the assertion embodied in equation (1), namely

$$(1) \qquad 1 + 3 + 5 + 7 + \cdots + (2n - 1) = n^2.$$

1°. We have already seen that equation (1) is true when $n = 1$.

2°. We now assume that $P(n)$ is true for the index $n = k$, *i.e.* we assume that indeed

$$(4) \qquad 1 + 3 + 5 + \cdots + (2k - 1) = k^2.$$

To obtain the sum of the first $k + 1$ odd integers we merely add the next odd one, $2k + 1$, to both sides of (4). This gives

$$1 + 3 + 5 + \cdots + (2k - 1) + (2k + 1) = k^2 + (2k + 1)$$
$$= (k + 1)^2.$$

But this equation is precisely equation (1) when the index n is $k + 1$, and hence we have shown that if the assertion is true for index k it is also true for index $k + 1$.

By the principle of mathematical induction this completes the proof that *equation (1) is valid for every positive integer n.* Q.E.D.

4. Further examples. We next prove that for every positive integer n

$$(5) \quad \frac{1}{1 \cdot 2} + \frac{1}{2 \cdot 3} + \frac{1}{3 \cdot 4} + \cdots + \frac{1}{n(n + 1)} = \frac{n}{n + 1}.$$

1°. For $n = 1$ the assertion of equation (5) is that

$$\frac{1}{1 \cdot 2} = \frac{1}{1+1}$$

and this is certainly the case.

2°. We assume that equation (5) is valid for index k. Thus we assume that

$$(6) \quad \frac{1}{1 \cdot 2} + \frac{1}{2 \cdot 3} + \frac{1}{3 \cdot 4} + \cdots + \frac{1}{k(k+1)} = \frac{k}{k+1}.$$

To obtain the left side of equation (5) for the index $n = k + 1$, we must add $1/(k+1)(k+2)$ to the left side of equation (6). Adding the same quantity to both sides gives

$$(7) \quad \frac{1}{1 \cdot 2} + \frac{1}{2 \cdot 3} + \frac{1}{3 \cdot 4} + \cdots + \frac{1}{k(k+1)} + \frac{1}{(k+1)(k+2)}$$

$$= \frac{k}{k+1} + \frac{1}{(k+1)(k+2)}$$

$$= \frac{k(k+2) + 1}{(k+1)(k+2)}$$

$$= \frac{k^2 + 2k + 1}{(k+1)(k+2)} = \frac{(k+1)^2}{(k+1)(k+2)}$$

$$= \frac{k+1}{(k+1)+1}.$$

But this is just equation (5) when the index n is $k + 1$. Hence by the principle of mathematical induction (5) is valid for every positive integer n. Q.E.D.

An assertion $P(n)$ may be false or meaningless for certain small values of n. In this case the assertion would necessarily be modified to state only what is actually true. Then the principle of mathematical induction would also be altered to meet the situation. Thus in step 1 of the process we would not set $n = 1$, but we would use instead the smallest integer for which the assertion is true. For example let us investigate the inequality[2]

---

[2] We assume that the reader has some familiarity with inequalities. A complete discussion is given in Chapter 4.

(8) $$2^n > 2n + 1.$$

For $n = 1$ this states that $2 > 3$ and this is false.

For $n = 2$ this states that $4 > 5$ and this is also false.

But for $n = 3$, the inequality asserts that $8 > 7$ and this is true.

Now assume that (8) is valid for the index $n = k$ where $k > 2$. Since $2^k > 2$ we may add[3] these terms to the assumed inequality $2^k > 2k + 1$ without disturbing the inequality. We find that

$$2^k + 2^k > 2k + 1 + 2$$
$$2^k \cdot 2 > 2(k + 1) + 1$$
$$2^{k+1} > 2(k + 1) + 1,$$

and this is just the inequality (8) when the index n is $k + 1$. Hence, using the principle of mathematical induction we have proved that *the inequality (8) is valid for every integer* $n \geqq 3$.

Exercise 1

In problems 1 through 14 prove that the assertion is true for all positive integers n.

1. The nth positive even integer is $2n$.

2. The nth positive odd integer is $2n - 1$.

3. $1 + 2 + 3 + 4 + \cdots + n = \dfrac{n(n + 1)}{2}$.

4. $1^2 + 2^2 + 3^2 + 4^2 + \cdots + n^2 = \dfrac{n(n + 1)(2n + 1)}{6}$.

5. $1 \cdot 2 + 2 \cdot 3 + 3 \cdot 4 + \cdots + n(n + 1)$
$$= \dfrac{n(n + 1)(n + 2)}{3}.$$

6. $1^2 + 3^2 + 5^2 + \cdots + (2n - 1)^2$
$$= \dfrac{n(2n - 1)(2n + 1)}{3}.$$

★7. $1^3 + 2^3 + 3^3 + \cdots + n^3 = \dfrac{n^2(n + 1)^2}{4}$.

---

[3] Here we use the obvious fact that if $a > c$ and $b > d$ then $a + b > c + d$ (see Chapter 4, theorem 4).

★8. $\dfrac{1}{1 \cdot 3} + \dfrac{1}{3 \cdot 5} + \dfrac{1}{5 \cdot 7} + \cdots + \dfrac{1}{(2n-1)(2n+1)}$
$$= \dfrac{n}{2n+1}.$$

★9. $\dfrac{1}{1 \cdot 4} + \dfrac{1}{4 \cdot 7} + \dfrac{1}{7 \cdot 10} + \cdots + \dfrac{1}{(3n-2)(3n+1)}$
$$= \dfrac{n}{3n+1}.$$

10. $1 + x + x^2 + \cdots + x^n = \dfrac{x^{n+1}-1}{x-1},$ if $x \neq 1.$

★11. $\dfrac{1}{x(x+1)} + \dfrac{1}{(x+1)(x+2)} + \cdots + \dfrac{1}{(x+n-1)(x+n)}$
$$= \dfrac{n}{x(x+n)}, \text{ if } x > 0.$$

★★12. $\dfrac{1}{n} + \dfrac{1}{n+1} + \dfrac{1}{n+2} + \cdots + \dfrac{1}{2n-1}$
$$= 1 - \dfrac{1}{2} + \dfrac{1}{3} - \dfrac{1}{4} + \cdots + \dfrac{1}{2n-1}.$$

★★13. $1^3 + 2^3 + 3^3 + \cdots + n^3 = (1 + 2 + 3 + \cdots + n)^2.$

14. $1 \cdot 3 + 3 \cdot 5 + 5 \cdot 7 + \cdots + (2n-1)(2n+1)$
$$= \dfrac{n(4n^2 + 6n - 1)}{3}.$$

15. For which positive integers n is $2^n > n^2$?

16. For which positive integers n is $2^n > n^3$?

★17. Prove that if $x > -1$ and n is an integer greater than 1, then $(1 + x)^n \geqq 1 + nx.$

★18. Prove that for $n \geqq 2$
$$\dfrac{1}{n+1} + \dfrac{1}{n+2} + \dfrac{1}{n+3} + \cdots + \dfrac{1}{2n} > \dfrac{13}{24}.$$

19. Prove that $1 + 5 + 9 + \cdots + 4n - 3 = n(2n-1).$

20. Prove that $3 \cdot 4 + 4 \cdot 7 + 5 \cdot 10 + \cdots$
$$+ (n+2)(3n+1) = n(n+2)(n+3).$$

★21. Prove the formula for the sum of the terms of an arithmetical progression
$$a + (a + d) + (a + 2d) + \cdots + (a + [n-1]d)$$
$$= n\left(a + \dfrac{(n-1)d}{2}\right).$$

Apply this formula to obtain the formulas of problems 3 and 19.

★**22.** Prove that $2 \cdot 2 + 3 \cdot 2^2 + 4 \cdot 2^3 + \cdots + (n+1)2^n = n2^{n+1}$.

★**23.** Prove that $x + y$ divides $x^{2n-1} + y^{2n-1}$ for each positive integer n.

★★**24.** Prove that if $x \neq \pm 1$, then

$$\frac{1}{1+x} + \frac{2}{1+x^2} + \frac{4}{1+x^4} + \cdots + \frac{2^n}{1+x^{2n}}$$
$$= \frac{1}{x-1} + \frac{2^{n+1}}{1-x^{2^{n+1}}}.$$

5. The factorial notation. It is convenient to have at hand a single symbol to represent the product of all the integers from 1 to n inclusive. The symbol universally used is $n!$ (read, "n factorial"). Thus by definition we have

$1! = 1$ $5! = 1 \cdot 2 \cdot 3 \cdot 4 \cdot 5 = 120$
$2! = 1 \cdot 2 = 2$ $6! = 1 \cdot 2 \cdot 3 \cdot 4 \cdot 5 \cdot 6 = 720$
$3! = 1 \cdot 2 \cdot 3 = 6$ $7! = 1 \cdot 2 \cdot 3 \cdot 4 \cdot 5 \cdot 6 \cdot 7 = 5040$
$4! = 1 \cdot 2 \cdot 3 \cdot 4 = 24$ $8! = 1 \cdot 2 \cdot 3 \cdot 4 \cdot 5 \cdot 6 \cdot 7 \cdot 8 = 40{,}320$

and in general

$$(9) \qquad n! = 1 \cdot 2 \cdot 3 \cdots (n-2)(n-1)n,$$

or what is the same thing

$$n! = n(n-1)(n-2) \cdots 3 \cdot 2 \cdot 1.$$

We observe that in general $(n+m)! \neq n! + m!$. For example if $n = 3$ and $m = 5$, the left side is $8! = 40{,}320$ and the right side is $3! + 5! = 6 + 120 = 126$. Certainly these are not equal.

Similarly we observe that $(2n)!$ and $2n!$ have different meanings. In the first expression the factorial applies to $2n$, while in the second expression we are to double $n!$. For example if $n = 3$, then $(2n)! = 6! = 720$, while on the other hand $2n! = 2 \cdot 3! = 2 \cdot 6 = 12$. Quite a difference!

In the same way we see that in general $n^2! \neq (n!)^2$. As an illustration take $n = 3$. Then $n^2! = 9! = 362{,}880$ and $(n!)^2 = (3!)^2 = 6^2 = 36$. These are far from being equal.

We leave it to the reader to check that the following assertions are true:

If $n > 1$, then $n \cdot (n-1)! = n!$,

If $n > 2$, then $(n^2 - n)(n-2)! = n!$,

If $n \geqq k$, then $(n - k + 1)n! + k \cdot n! = (n+1)!$,

If $n > 2$, then $n! - (n-1)! = (n-1)^2 \cdot (n-2)!$.

Exercise 2

1. Find all positive integers n for which $(2n)! = 2n!$.

2. Are there any positive integers n such that $(3n)! = 3n!$?

3. Find all pairs of positive integers m and n such that $(m+n)! = m! + n!$

4. Solve the equation $(n+2)! = 90n!$ for n.

★5. Prove that if $2 \leqq k \leqq n - 1$, then

$$\frac{n!}{(n-k)!k!} + \frac{n!}{(n-k+1)!(k-1)!} = \frac{(n+1)!}{(n-k+1)!k!}.$$

★6. Prove that $1 \cdot 1! + 2 \cdot 2! + 3 \cdot 3! + \cdots + n \cdot n! = (n+1)! - 1$. *Hint:* Use mathematical induction.

★7. Prove that

$$\frac{3!}{1!} + \frac{4!}{2!} + \frac{5!}{3!} + \cdots + \frac{n!}{(n-2)!} = \frac{n^3 - n - 6}{3}.$$

6. The Pascal triangle. The expression $(x+y)^n$ occurs so frequently in mathematics that it pays to have a systematic method of writing down the expansion of this expression. By direct (and for higher values of n laborious) computation, we find that

$$(x+y)^0 = 1$$
$$(x+y)^1 = x + y$$
$$(x+y)^2 = x^2 + 2xy + y^2$$
$$(x+y)^3 = x^3 + 3x^2y + 3xy^2 + y^3$$
$$(x+y)^4 = x^4 + 4x^3y + 6x^2y^2 + 4xy^3 + y^4$$
$$(x+y)^5 = x^5 + 5x^4y + 10x^3y^2 + 10x^2y^3 + 5xy^4 + y^5$$
$$(x+y)^6 = x^6 + 6x^5y + 15x^4y^2 + 20x^3y^3 + 15x^2y^4 + 6xy^5 + y^6.$$

Can we predict the expansion of $(x+y)^7$ from a study of these expansions?

The pattern of the powers of x and y is clearly discernible. Indeed in going from left to right the powers of x decrease from n to 0 and the powers of y increase from 0 to n. Thus, ignoring the coefficients (the numbers that multiply x and y), we have

$$(x + y)^n \sim x^n + x^{n-1}y + x^{n-2}y^2 + \cdots$$
$$+ x^{n-k}y^k + \cdots + y^n.$$

Therefore, in analyzing the triangular array above we may omit the letters x and y and write only the coefficients as shown in Figure 2.1. A close inspection of this array allows us to guess a law of formation. First the sides of the triangular array are formed by ones. Second, each number inside the triangle is the sum of the two numbers which appear in the line above just to the left and to the right of the number. For example in the seventh row, the row for $(x + y)^6$, we have $6 = 1 + 5$, $15 = 5 + 10$, $20 = 10 + 10$, etc.

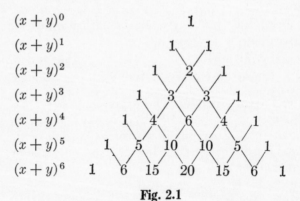

Fig. 2.1

Is this simple rule of formation valid if the triangular array is extended downward to include higher powers of $x + y$? If we wanted the coefficients for $(x + y)^7$ could we write $1 + 6 = 7$, $6 + 15 = 21$, $15 + 20 = 35$, etc., and then conclude that

$$(x + y)^7 = x^7 + 7x^6y + 21x^5y^2 + 35x^4y^3$$
$$+ 35x^3y^4 + 21x^2y^5 + 7xy^6 + y^7?$$

The answer is yes, and the proof can be given by mathematical induction. However, instead of writing out the general case we will merely indicate the step from $(x + y)^5$ to $(x + y)^6$. The discerning student will observe that the pattern is the same in going from $(x + y)^n$ to $(x + y)^{n+1}$.

Indeed

$$(x + y)^6 = (x + y)(x + y)^5$$
$$= x(x + y)^5 + y(x + y)^5.$$

We assume that

$$(x + y)^5 = x^5 + 5x^4y + 10x^3y^2 + 10x^2y^3 + 5xy^4 + y^5.$$

Then we have

(10) $\quad x(x + y)^5 = x^6 + 5x^5y + 10x^4y^2 + 10x^3y^3 + 5x^2y^4 + xy^5$

(11) $\quad y(x + y)^5 = x^5y + 5x^4y^2 + 10x^3y^3 + 10x^2y^4 + 5xy^5 + y^6$.

(12) $\quad (x + y)^6 = x^6 + 6x^5y + 15x^4y^2 + 20x^3y^3 + 15x^2y^4 + 6xy^5 + y^6$

Notice that in adding equations (10) and (11) to obtain (12) the method of forming the coefficients is exactly that described for the array of Figure 2.1, namely $1 + 5 = 6$, $5 + 10 = 15$, $10 + 10 = 20$, etc. $\qquad$ Q.E.D.

The array of Figure 2.1 is known as Pascal's triangle in honor of Blaise Pascal (1623–1662) who first discovered this convenient arrangement of the coefficients. The numbers in this array are known as the binomial coefficients, because they appear as the coefficients in the expansion of the binomial $(x + y)^n$.

This pattern may be applied in a variety of situations.

Example 1. Expand $(2A + B)^3$.
Solution. Set $x = 2A$ and $y = B$ and use the fourth line of Pascal's triangle. We have

$$(2A + B)^3 = 1(2A)^3 + 3(2A)^2B + 3(2A)B^2 + B^3$$
$$= 8A^3 + 12A^2B + 6AB^2 + B^3.$$

Example 2. Expand $(A - 3B)^4$.
Solution. We can write $(A - 3B)^4 = (A + (-3B))^4$ and set $x = A$ and $y = -3B$. Then using the fifth line of

the Pascal triangle, we find

$$(A - 3B)^4 = A^4 + 4A^3(-3B) + 6A^2(-3B)^2$$
$$+ 4A(-3B)^3 + (-3B)^4$$
$$= A^4 - 12A^3B + 54A^2B^2 - 108AB^3 + 81B^4.$$

Exercise 3

1. Extend Pascal's triangle and find the coefficients in the expansion of $(x + y)^8$ and $(x + y)^9$.
2. Find the coefficient of x^3y^2 in $(3x - 2y)^5$.
3. Find the coefficient of x^2y^5 in $\left(\dfrac{x}{2} - \dfrac{y}{3}\right)^7$.
4. Prove that for any integer n, the quantity $(2n + 1)^2 - 1$ is divisible by 8.
5. Prove that if you square any odd number and then subtract one, the result is divisible by 8.
6. Prove that for any integer n, the quantity $(3n - 1)^3 + 1$ is divisible by $9n$ but is not divisible by $18n$.
7. Prove that the sum of the cubes of any three consecutive positive integers is always divisible by three times the middle one.
★8. Prove that the sum of the numbers in the nth row of Pascal's triangle is 2^{n-1}.

★7. The binomial coefficients. The numbers which appear in Pascal's triangle are so important and so interesting that it is worthwhile to have a special symbol for them.

Definition 1. *The symbol* $\dbinom{n}{k}$ *(read, "n above k") represents the coefficient of* $x^{n-k}y^k$ *in the expansion of* $(x + y)^n$.

Thus by the very definition of the symbol we have

$$(13) \quad (x + y)^n = \binom{n}{0}x^n + \binom{n}{1}x^{n-1}y + \binom{n}{2}x^{n-2}y^2 + \cdots$$
$$+ \binom{n}{k}x^{n-k}y^k + \binom{n}{k+1}x^{n-k-1}y^{k+1}$$
$$+ \cdots + \binom{n}{n}y^n.$$

In particular we conclude from $(x + y)^2 = x^2 + 2xy + y^2$ that

$$\binom{2}{0} = 1, \qquad \binom{2}{1} = 2, \qquad \binom{2}{2} = 1.$$

Our objective is to obtain a formula which allows us to compute $\binom{n}{k}$ directly, without recourse to Pascal's triangle. We will need the definition

$$(14) \qquad\qquad 0! = 1.$$

With this definition the obvious formula

$$(15) \qquad\qquad n! = n \cdot (n - 1)!$$

which is valid for any integer $n \geqq 2$, is now also valid when $n = 1$. In fact this is one of the reasons for the definition (14).

Theorem 1. *For any positive integer n, and any integer k such that $0 \leqq k \leqq n$,*

$$(16) \qquad\qquad \binom{n}{k} = \frac{n!}{k!(n-k)!}.$$

Proof. The proof is by induction. Let $n = 1$. Then (recalling that $0! = 1$) we have

$$\binom{1}{0} = \frac{1!}{0!(1-0)!} = \frac{1}{1 \cdot 1} = 1$$

and

$$\binom{1}{1} = \frac{1!}{1!(1-1)!} = \frac{1}{1 \cdot 1} = 1.$$

But these are the coefficients in the expansion $(x + y)^1 = 1 \cdot x + 1 \cdot y$.

Before proceeding to the general case we need to consider the special values $k = 0$ and $k = n$. We observe that when $k = 0$ we have

$$\binom{n}{0} = \frac{n!}{0!(n-0)!} = \frac{n!}{1 \cdot n!} = 1,$$

and when $k = n$ we have

$$\binom{n}{n} = \frac{n!}{n!(n-n)!} = \frac{n!}{n! \cdot 1} = 1.$$

But these are indeed the coefficients of x^n and y^n respectively in the expansion of $(x + y)^n$, so that in this case equation (16) is valid.

We now suppose that the formula (16) is valid for index n, and we proceed to multiply both sides of equation (13) by $x + y$. The left side yields $(x + y)^{n+1}$, and the right side gives the expansion. Let us concentrate our attention on the terms which yield $x^{n-k}y^{k+1}$. This type of term arises in only two ways, namely from

$$y\binom{n}{k}x^{n-k}y^k = \binom{n}{k}x^{n-k}y^{k+1},$$

and from

$$x\binom{n}{k+1}x^{n-k-1}y^{k+1} = \binom{n}{k+1}x^{n-k}y^{k+1}.$$

On adding these terms it is clear that the coefficient of $x^{n-k}y^{k+1}$ is

(17) $$\binom{n}{k} + \binom{n}{k+1}$$

and by definition this is represented by the symbol $\binom{n+1}{k+1}$.

Therefore

(18) $$\binom{n+1}{k+1} = \binom{n}{k} + \binom{n}{k+1}.$$

We are assuming that the formula (16) is valid for all integers up to and including n. Hence

(19) $$\binom{n}{k} = \frac{n!}{k!(n-k)!}$$

and

(20) $$\binom{n}{k+1} = \frac{n!}{(k+1)!(n-k-1)!}.$$

Consequently from equations (18), (19), and (20) we find that

$$\binom{n+1}{k+1} = \frac{n!}{k!(n-k)!} + \frac{n!}{(k+1)!(n-k-1)!}$$
$$= \frac{n!(k+1)}{(k+1)!(n-k)!} + \frac{n!(n-k)}{(k+1)!(n-k)!}$$
$$= \frac{n!(k+1+n-k)}{(k+1)!(n-k)!} = \frac{n!(n+1)}{(k+1)!(n-k)!}$$
$$= \frac{(n+1)!}{(k+1)!(n+1-(k+1))!}.$$

But this last expression is just equation (16) when the upper index is $n+1$ and the lower index is $k+1$. Q.E.D.

Example. Find the coefficient of x^7y^3 in the expansion of $(x+y)^{10}$.

Solution. Here $n=10$, and $k=3$. The coefficient is

$$\binom{10}{3} = \frac{10!}{3!(10-3)!} = \frac{10 \cdot 9 \cdot 8 \cdot 7 \cdot 6 \cdot 5 \cdot 4 \cdot 3 \cdot 2 \cdot 1}{3 \cdot 2 \cdot 1 \cdot 7 \cdot 6 \cdot 5 \cdot 4 \cdot 3 \cdot 2 \cdot 1} = 120.$$

Exercise 4

1. Prove that $\binom{n}{k} = \binom{n}{n-k}$.

2. Find the coefficient of $A^{10}B^4$ in the expansion of $(A-B)^{14}$.

3. Find the coefficient of A^5B^9 in the same expansion.

4. Prove that

$$\binom{n}{0} + \binom{n}{1} + \binom{n}{2} + \cdots + \binom{n}{n} = 2^n.$$

5. Prove that

$$\binom{n}{0} - \binom{n}{1} + \binom{n}{2} - \binom{n}{3} + \cdots + (-1)^n\binom{n}{n} = 0.$$

CHAPTER 3

Magic Squares

1. The simplest magic square. Let us examine the bers in Figure 3.1, which have been arranged in the form of a square. We observe that if we add the numbers in each row we have:

$$\begin{array}{ccc} 6 & 7 & 2 \\ 1 & 5 & 9 \\ 8 & 3 & 4 \end{array}$$

Fig. 3.1

(1) $6 + 7 + 2 = 15$, $1 + 5 + 9 = 15$ and $8 + 3 + 4 = 15$.

The sum is the same each time. This is not surprising. If we add the numbers in each column we have:

(2) $6 + 1 + 8 = 15$, $7 + 5 + 3 = 15$ and $2 + 9 + 4 = 15$.

This is more surprising. If we add the numbers in the diagonals we have:

(3) $6 + 5 + 4 = 15$ and $2 + 5 + 8 = 15$

In all 8 of these sums we have the same answer of 15. This is *indeed surprising*.

The array in Figure 3.1 is an example of a magic square of third order.

Definition 1. *An array of n^2 numbers in the form of a square of n numbers on each side is called a magic square of order n, if there is constant S (the sum) for which*

(1) *The sum of the numbers in each row is S,*
(2) *The sum of the numbers in each column is S,*

40

(3) *The sum of the numbers in the diagonal descending from the left to right (the main diagonal) is S,*

(4) *The sum of the numbers in the diagonal descending from right to left (the second diagonal) is S.*

The common sum S is called the magic constant.

Returning to our example, we see that once we have a magic square it is possible to find many other magic squares of the same order. For example we could add the same number to each number of the square. If we add 3 to each number in our original square we get the magic square shown in Figure 3.2. In this square the sum of the numbers in each row, or in each column, or in each diagonal must be 24 since we added 3 in each place and $15 + 3 \times 3 = 24$.

Similarly if we double each of the numbers in the magic square shown in Figure 3.2, we must obtain another magic square for which $S = 48 = 2 \times 24$. This square array is shown in Figure 3.3.

9	10	5
4	8	12
11	6	7

Fig. 3.2

18	20	10
8	16	24
22	12	14

Fig. 3.3

There are still other ways of obtaining a magic square from the one shown in Figure 3.1. We could merely rotate the figure about the center through some multiple of 90°, or we could interchange the first and last rows, or we could interchange the first and last columns. Figure 3.4 shows the magic square obtained from that of Figure 3.1 by a rotation of 90° in the counter-clockwise direction, and Figure 3.5 shows the magic square obtained by interchanging the first and last rows.

2	9	4
7	5	3
6	1	8

Fig. 3.4

8	3	4
1	5	9
6	7	2

Fig. 3.5

The numbers 1, 2, 3, · · ·, 9 used in the magic square in Figure 3.1, form an arithmetic progression. In Figure 3.2 the numbers are 4, 5, 6, · · ·, 12 and these also form an arithmetic progression. This is also the case for the numbers 8, 10, 12, · · ·, 24 of Figure 3.3 where now the common difference is 2. It is obvious that if we start with the magic square of Figure 3.1 and perform any sequence of operations: (a) add a constant to each number in the magic square; (b) multiply each number in the magic square by a constant—the result will always be a magic square for which the numbers form an arithmetic progression. One might at first be tempted to say that in any magic square of third order the numbers must form an arithmetic progression. The square shown in Figure 3.6, shows that this conjecture is false. An analysis of **all** magic squares of the third order is somewhat complicated (and we postpone it till later), but if we restrict ourselves to studying just those magic squares of third order for which

7	9	2
1	6	11
10	3	5

Fig. 3.6

A	B	C
D	E	F
G	H	I

Fig. 3.7

the elements form an arithmetic progression, then we can find all of them. It turns out that *every such magic square can be obtained from the one shown in Figure 3.1 by means of the operations we have already described, namely (a) additions (b) multiplications (c) rotations (d) interchanges of the first and third rows or interchanges of the first and third columns.* We proceed to prove this theorem.

Suppose we have at hand such a magic square. If a is the smallest number appearing in the square, we first subtract a from each element of the square. The elements of the new square still form an arithmetic progression and if d is the common difference in this arithmetic progression then the nine elements will be 0, d, $2d$, · · ·, $8d$. If we divide each element by d, and then add 1 to each element we have a magic square formed from the numbers 1, 2, 3,

$\cdots$, 9. The position of these numbers is unknown. Let us denote them by the letters A, B, C, $\cdots$, I as shown in Fig. 3.7.

We next show that S, the common sum, must be 15. The sums on the rows give:

$$A + B + C = S. \quad D + E + F = S. \quad G + H + I = S.$$

Whence on adding all of these equations we find that:

$$A + B + C + D + E + F + G + H + I = 3S.$$

But these are the numbers 1, 2, 3, $\cdots$, 9 in some order and since $1 + 2 + 3 + \cdots + 9 = 45$, we have $3S = 45$, or $S = 15$.

We now prove that $E = 5$. Indeed by the definition of a magic square we have:

$$\begin{aligned} D + E + F &= 15, \\ B + E + H &= 15, \\ A + E + I &= 15, \\ C + E + G &= 15. \end{aligned}$$

Adding these equations gives:

$$A + B + C + D + E + F + G + H + I + 3E = 60,$$
$$45 \qquad\qquad\qquad + 3E = 60,$$
$$3E = 15,$$

and hence $E = 5$.

As a result the various pairs of letters which are separated by E must add up to 10. Thus $A + I$, $B + H$, $C + G$, and $D + F$, are each 10, and in some order (as yet unknown) they must be $1 + 9$, $2 + 8$, $3 + 7$, and $4 + 6$.

We next prove that the number 1 cannot appear in any corner. For if so, we could by a rotation put it in the upper left-hand corner. Thus let us suppose that $A = 1$. Then it follows that $I = 9$. Now if 2, 3, or 4 were in the same row with 1, then the third number of that row must be either 12, 11 or 10 in order to have a sum of 15 for the row, and since we have only the numbers 1 through 9 at our disposal, we cannot have 2, 3, or 4 in the top row. Similarly these three numbers cannot appear in the first column. That leaves only the *two* places F and H for the *three* numbers 2, 3, and 4 (since we already have $E = 5$ and $I = 9$). But this is impossible, and hence the number 1 cannot be a corner number.

Since 1 must be either D, B, F, or G, we can, by making a suitable rotation, assume that $D = 1$. Then we immediately have $F = 9$ (since $D + E + F = 1 + 5 + F = 15$).

Next we locate 7. This number 7 cannot be in the same column with 9, because the sum would already exceed 15. It cannot be in the same column with 1 since $1 + 7 + 7 = 15$, so that the third number in that column would also be 7, and this is impossible since the numbers from 1 through 9 are to be used once and only once. Thus 7 must be in the second column, either B or H. Now by an interchange of the first and third rows we can place the 7 in the first row if it should happen to fall in the third row. Since $B + E + H = 7 + 5 + H = 15$, we must have $H = 3$. Summarizing, we have proved so far that a magic square of the third order formed from the numbers 1 through 9 must have the form shown in Figure 3.8 (except possibly for rotations and the interchange of the first and third rows). The fact that the rows and diagonals each add to 15, now gives:

$$A + C = 8,$$
$$A + I = 10,$$
$$C + I = 6.$$

A	7	C
1	5	9
G	3	I

Fig. 3.8

These three equations have the unique solution $A = 6$, $C = 2$, $I = 4$. The only number not now placed is 8, so $G = 8$. Then Figure 3.8 gives the same magic square as Figure 3.1.

We have proved the following

Theorem. *Every magic square of third order in which the 9 elements form an arithmetic progression, can be obtained from the magic square of Figure 3.1 by an appropriate sequence of operations of the following type:*

(a) *Adding a constant to each element of the square,*

(b) *Multiplying each element of the square by a constant,*

(c) *Interchanging the first and third row,*

(d) *Interchanging the first and third column.*

Exercise 1

1. Show that it is impossible to form a magic square of second order from the numbers 1, 2, 3, and 4.

2. Show that it is impossible to have a magic square of second order in which the four elements form an arithmetic progression, except in the case that all of the numbers are the same.

★3. The magic squares shown in Figures 3.1, 3.4, and 3.5 are different arrangements of the same magic square. There are exactly 8 such arrangements all different. Find the remaining 5 arrangements.

4. Show that if the numbers 1 through 16 are used to form a magic square (fourth order) then the sum of the elements in any one row or column (the magic constant) is 34.

5. What is the magic constant if a fifth order magic square is made from the numbers 1 through 25?

★6. Prove that if the numbers 1 through n^2 are used to form a magic square of nth order, then the magic constant is $n(n^2 + 1)/2$.

2. Panmagic squares. If we look at the fourth order square shown in Figure 3.9 we see that the elements A, F, K, and Q form the main diagonal, and D, G, J and M form the other diagonal. We can find still other diagonals if we allow them to be broken, for example we can agree that B, G, L, and M form a broken diagonal. To be precise about this matter let us imagine that the square is

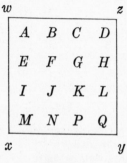

Fig. 3.9

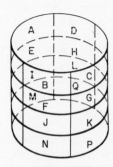

Fig. 3.10

rolled up and the edges joined (the edge yz to the edge xw) forming a cylinder as shown in Figure 3.10.

In that figure the letters and lines in back are shown dotted, and the letters are reversed for easier reading. On the cylinder there is no distinction between the diagonal $A\ F\ K\ Q$ and $B\ G\ L\ M$. This suggests

Definition 2. *For a square array a set of elements which forms a diagonal on the cylinder, and does not form a diagonal on the square, is called a broken diagonal of the square array.*

The definition refers to a square of any size. It is easy to see that for the particular array of Figure 3.9, there are 6 broken diagonals: the 3 descending from the left to right are $B\ G\ L\ M$, $C\ H\ I\ N$, and $D\ E\ J\ P$; and the three descending from right to left are $C\ F\ I\ Q$, $B\ E\ L\ P$ and $A\ H\ K\ N$.

Definition 3. *A square array of numbers is called a panmagic square (perfect square, diabolic square[1]) if there is a constant S (the magic constant) such that:*

(1) *The sum of the numbers in each row is S,*
(2) *The sum of the numbers in each column is S,*
(3) *The sum of the numbers in each diagonal is S,*
(4) *The sum of the numbers in each broken diagonal is S.*

It may seem a remarkable fact that such magic squares exist. A panmagic square of fourth order is shown in Figure 3.11 where $S = 34$, and one of fifth order is shown in Figure 3.12 where $S = 65$.

1	8	13	12
15	10	3	6
4	5	16	9
14	11	2	7

1	14	22	10	18
7	20	3	11	24
13	21	9	17	5
19	2	15	23	6
25	8	16	4	12

Fig. 3.11   **Fig. 3.12**

[1]These squares are frequently called Nasik squares. The term Nasik was introduced by A. H. Frost who made contributions to the general theory of magic squares while living in Nasik, India. (See *Quarterly Journal of Mathematics*, vol. 7 [1866] pp. 92–102.)

How about a panmagic square of third order? If we use the letters A through I as unknowns, as indicated in Figure 3.7, we have 9 unknowns. We presume that S, the sum, is known. Then from the rows we have 3 equations, from the columns we have 3 equations and from the diagonals in both directions, broken or not, we have 6 more equations. Thus in all we have 12 equations in 9 unknowns. Although some of these equations may be *redundant* (obtainable from the others) this nevertheless suggests that we have too many equations for the number of unknowns, and that no solutions exist. In fact it can be proved that the only panmagic square of third order is the one in which all of the 9 elements are the same. The details of this proof are left for the reader, and an outline of the method is given as problem 4 of exercise 2.

Let us do the same type of counting for a panmagic square of nth order. The number of unknowns is obviously n^2. The sums taken on the n rows yield n equations, and similarly for the columns. Further there are n diagonals (broken or otherwise) descending from left to right, and n more descending from right to left. Thus in all there are $4n$ equations to be solved for n^2 unknowns. Thus if:

$$(4) \qquad\qquad 4n < n^2$$

we may expect to find nontrivial solutions (*i.e.* the elements all different) and the number of solutions may be expected to increase with the difference between n^2 and $4n$.

In the particular case that $n = 3$, the inequality (4) is not satisfied, since $12 > 3^2$, and when $n = 4$ we have $4 \cdot 4 = 4^2$. But for $n = 5$, the inequality (4) is satisfied, and indeed as n increases so also does $n^2 - 4n$. Thus we may expect that as n increases, the number of different panmagic squares increases, and this is indeed the case.

3. A general formula for magic squares. We can give all of the magic squares of third order. Indeed we will indicate in problems 2 and 3 of exercise 2 the proof that all such magic squares are given by the array shown in Figure 3.13. By this we mean two things: (1) If any three numbers are used for t, a, and b, in Figure 3.13, the result is a magic square of third order, (2) Given any magic square of third order, it is possible to find values for t, a, and b, such that the array of Figure 3.13 generates the given magic square. For example: $t = 6$, $a = 1$, $b = -4$ will generate the magic square of Figure 3.6.

The magic squares generated by the array of Figure 3.13, form what is called a *three-parameter* family

$t + a$	$t - a - b$	$t + b$
$t - a + b$	t	$t + a - b$
$t - b$	$t + a + b$	$t - a$

Fig. 3.13

of magic squares, and the three variables a, b, and t are called the *parameters*.

A similar formula for fourth order magic squares is shown in Figure 3.14. Here we have an eight-parameter family of magic squares, and the eight parameters are W, X, Y, Z, A, B, C and D. The assertion is that we can assign to these variables any eight numbers we please and the result will be a magic square with $S = W + X + Y + Z$ as the magic constant. Conversely given any magic square of fourth order we can obtain it from the array of Figure 3.12 by choosing the parameters W, X, $\cdots$, D properly. The proof of this assertion is somewhat long and a little complicated, so we omit it.

$W + A$	$X - A + B$	$Y - B + C$	$Z - C$
$Z - A + D$	Y	X	$W + A - D$
$X - C - D$	W	Z	$Y + C + D$
$Y + C$	$Z + A - B$	$W + B - C$	$X - A$

Fig. 3.14

Exercise 2

1. Find the values of t, a, and b, for the array in Figure 3.13, such that it generates the magic square shown in (a) Figure 3.1, (b) Figure 3.2, (c) Figure 3.3, (d) Figure 3.4, (e) Figure 3.5.

2. Prove that the square in Figure 3.13 is a magic square for any three numbers t, a, and b, and that the magic constant $S = 3t$.

★★**3.** By following the steps indicated below prove the converse, namely that any third order magic square can be generated from the array of Figure 3.13 by a proper choice of t, a, and b:

> (a) Assume the given magic square has the form indicated in Figure 3.7, where now the letters $A, B, C, \cdots, I$ are given numbers.
>
> (b) Prove that if we set $3t = S$, i.e. if we take $t = \dfrac{S}{3}$, then we must have $E = t$.
>
> (c) Now define a by the equation $a = A - t$. Then obviously $A = t + a$.
>
> (d) Now use the result of step (c) to prove that $I = t - a$.
>
> (e) Define b by the equation $b = C - t$. Then obviously $C = t + b$.
>
> (f) Use the result of step (e) to prove that $G = t - b$.
>
> (g) Use the results of steps (c) and (f) to prove that $D = t - a + b$.
>
> (h) Use the results of steps (d) and (e) to prove that $F = t + a - b$.
>
> (i) Use the results of steps (d) and (f) to prove that $H = t + a + b$. This completes the proof of the theorem. Why?

4. Prove that there are no panmagic squares of third order except the trivial ones in which all of the elements are the same. *Hint*: Use the result of problem 3, and show that the array of Figure 3.13 is panmagic only when $a = b = 0$.

5. Show that if the square of Figure 3.9 is rolled up vertically rather than horizontally, i.e. if the edge xy is joined to the edge wz, then the diagonals on the cylinder formed in this way, are identical with the diagonals of the cylinder of Figure 3.10. Is this also true for a 5 × 5 square?

6. If in Figure 3.14 we set $W = 6$, $X = 11$, $Y = 10$, $Z = 7$, $A = 10$, $B = 2$, $C = -6$, and $D = 8$, we obtain a magic square which appears on a famous woodcut by Albrecht Dürer made in the sixteenth century. Find this magic square.

7. What values should we assign to the eight parameters of Figure 3.14 in order to obtain the magic square in Figure 3.15.?

3	10	16	5
13	8	2	11
6	15	9	4
12	1	7	14

Fig. 3.15

8. Prove that the array of Figure 3.14 will always give a magic square but will not always give a panmagic square.

9. What values should we assign to the eight parameters of Figure 3.14 in order to obtain the panmagic square of Figure 3.11?

4. Magic cubes. By a magic cube of nth order, we quite naturally mean an arrangement of n^3 numbers in a cubical array such that the sum of the numbers in any column, or in any row, or in any 3-dimensional diagonal is the same. The general theory of such cubes is quite difficult so we will be content with giving just one example.

If we look at the cube of third order shown in Figure 3.16, all of the numbers are not visible, so we must pull it apart so that it forms three layers in order to see the rest of the numbers. Clearly this splitting into layers can be done in three different ways, as is indicated in Figures 3.17, 3.18, and 3.19. In order to simplify the terminology we have added three mutually perpendicular lines known as the x-, y-, and z-axes. In this way we can refer to the

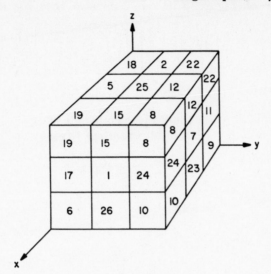

Fig. 3.16

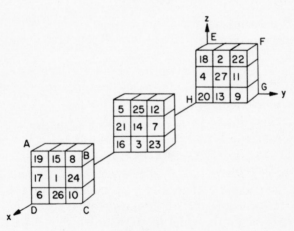

Fig. 3.17

horizontal layers as layers formed by planes perpendicular
to the z-axis. But there are two different types of vertical
layers, and we can now distinguish between them, since
one type is formed by planes perpendicular to the x-axis
(front, middle, back) and the other is formed by planes
perpendicular to the y-axis (left, middle, right).

18	2	22
5	25	12
19	15	8

19	5	18
17	21	4
6	16	20

15	25	2
1	14	27
26	3	13

8	12	22
24	7	11
10	23	9

Top Layer   Left Layer   Middle Layer   Right Layer

4	27	11
21	14	7
17	1	24

Planes perpendicular to the y-axis.
Vertical Layers.

Fig. 3.19

Middle Layer

20	13	9
16	3	23
6	26	10

Bottom Layer

Planes perpendicular
to the z-axis.
Horizontal layers.

Fig. 3.18

The magic cube shown in Figures 3.16 and 3.17 utilizes the numbers $1, 2, 3, \cdots, 27$. If S is the magic constant then the sum of the numbers in all of the 9 vertical columns must be $9S$. But this is just the sum of the numbers $1, 2, 3, \cdots, 27$, therefore:

$$9S = 1 + 2 + 3 + \cdots + 27 = \frac{27 \times 28}{2} = 27 \times 14,$$

and hence $S = 3 \times 14 = 42$.

Inspection of the various layers shows that the sum in each row or column is 42. (There are $3 \times 9 = 27$ such sums to check.) For the 3-dimensional diagonals we have (see Figure 3.17)

A G	$19 + 14 + 9 = 42,$
B H	$8 + 14 + 20 = 42,$
C E	$10 + 14 + 18 = 42,$
D F	$6 + 14 + 22 = 42.$

So by definition we have a magic cube.

One should observe that the layers by themselves are *not* magic squares. They are magic in the rows and columns, but not in the diagonals. Suppose we asked for a magic cube of third order, such that every plane section forms a magic square of third order. It can be proved that no such magic cube exists, except for the trivial one in which all of the numbers are the same. The proof of this result is a little difficult and tedious so we omit it, but the proof can be given using the representation for third order magic squares shown in Figure 3.13.

5. An old letter. The following letter is copied from "Letters and papers on Philosophical subjects by Benjamin Franklin, Ll.D., F.R.S.," published in England in 1769.

From Benjamin Franklin, Esq. of Philadelphia,

To Peter Collinson, Esq. at London.

Dear Sir:—According to your request I now send you the arithmetical curiosity of which this is the history.

Being one day in the country at the house of our common friend, the late learned Mr. Logan, he showed me a folio French book filled with magic squares, wrote, if I forget not, by one Mr. Frenicle, in which he said the author had discovered great ingenuity and dexterity in the management of numbers; and though several other foreigners had distinguished themselves in the same way, he did not recollect that any one Englishman had done anything of the kind remarkable.

I said it was perhaps a mark of the good sense of our mathematicians that they would not spend their time in things that were merely *difficiles nugae*, incapable of any useful application. He answered that many of the arithmetical or mathematical questions publicly proposed in England were equally trifling and useless. Perhaps the considering and answering such questions, I replied, may not be altogether useless if it produces by practice an habitual readiness and exactness in mathematical disquisitions, which readiness may, on many occasions be of real use. In the same way says he, may the making of these squares be of use. I then confessed to him that in my younger days, having once some leisure (which I still think

I might have employed more usefully) I had amused myself in making these kind of magic squares, and, at length had acquired such a knack at it, that I could fill the cells of any magic square of reasonable size with a series of numbers as fast as I could write them, disposed in such a manner that the sums of every row, horizontal, perpendicular or diagonal should be equal; but not being satisfied with these, which I looked on as common and easy things, I had imposed on myself more difficult tasks, and succeeded in making other magic squares with a variety of properties and much more curious. He then showed me several in the same book of an uncommon and more curious kind; but as I thought none of them equal to some I remembered to have made, he desired me to let him see them; and accordingly the next time I visited him, I carried him a square of 8 which I found among my old papers, and which I will now give you, with an account of its properties. [See Figure 3.20].

52	61	4	13	20	29	36	45
14	3	62	51	46	35	30	19
53	60	5	12	21	28	37	44
11	6	59	54	43	38	27	22
55	58	7	10	23	26	39	42
9	8	57	56	41	40	25	24
50	63	2	15	18	31	34	47
16	1	64	49	48	33	32	17

Fig. 3.20

The properties are:

1. That every straight row (horizontal or vertical) of 8 numbers added together makes 260, and half of each row, half of 260.

2. That the bent row of 8 numbers ascending diagonally, viz., from 16 ascending to 10 and from 23 descending to 17 and every one of its parallel bent rows of 8 numbers

X   Y

200	217	232	249	8	25	40	57	72	89	104	121	136	153	168	185
58	39	26	7	250	231	218	199	186	167	154	135	122	103	90	71
198	219	230	251	6	27	38	59	70	91	102	123	134	155	166	187
60	37	28	5	252	229	220	197	188	165	156	133	124	101	92	69
201	216	233	248	9	24	41	56	73	88	105	120	137	152	169	184
55	42	23	10	247	234	215	202	183	170	151	138	119	106	87	74
203	214	235	246	11	22	43	54	75	86	107	118	139	150	171	182
53	44	21	12	245	236	213	204	181	172	149	140	117	108	85	76
205	212	237	244	13	20	45	52	77	84	109	116	141	148	173	180
51	46	19	14	243	238	211	206	179	174	147	142	115	110	83	78
207	210	239	242	15	18	47	50	79	82	111	114	143	146	175	178
49	48	17	16	241	240	209	208	177	176	145	144	113	112	81	80
196	221	228	253	4	29	36	61	68	93	100	125	132	157	164	189
62	35	30	3	254	227	222	195	190	163	158	131	126	99	94	67
194	223	226	255	2	31	34	63	66	95	98	127	130	159	162	191
64	33	32	1	256	225	224	193	192	161	160	129	128	97	96	65

Z   W

Fig. 3.21

make 260, etc., etc. And last the four corner numbers with
the four middle numbers make 260. So this magical square
seems perfect in its kind, but these are not all of its properties, there are 5 other curious ones which at some time I
will explain to you.

Mr. Logan then showed me an old arithmetic book in
quarto, wrote, I think by one Stifelius, which contained a
square of 16 which he said he should imagine to be a work
of great labour; but if I forget not, it had only the common
properties of making the same sum, viz., 2056 in every
row, horizontal, vertical, and diagonal. Not willing to be
outdone by Mr. Stifelius, even in the size of my square, I
went home, and made that evening the following magical
square of 16 [see Figure 3.21] which besides having all the
properties of the foregoing square of 8, i.e., it would make
2056 in all the same rows and diagonals, had this added,
that a four-square hole being cut in a piece of paper of such
a size as to take in and show through it just 16 of the little
squares, when laid on the greater square, the sum of the
16 numbers so appearing through the hole, wherever it
was placed on the greater square should likewise make

2056. This I sent to our friend the next morning, who after some days sent it back in a letter with these words:
"I return to thee thy astonishing
"or most stupendous piece
"of the magical square in which"
—but the compliment is too extravagant and therefore, for his sake as well as for my own I ought not to repeat it. Nor is it necessary, for I make no question but you will readily allow the square of 16 to be the most magically magical square ever made by any magician.

I am etc.
B. F.

6. More and deeper. We have given only a brief introduction to the theory of magic squares. The reader who wishes to pursue the matter further and deeper, will find a more extensive account of this subject, together with a tremendous amount of other fascinating matter in either of the following two books:

Maurice Kraitchik, *Mathematical Recreations*, 2nd ed. (New York: Dover Publications, Inc., 1953).

W. W. R. Ball, *Mathematical Recreations and Essays* (London: Macmillan and Co. Ltd., 1914).

Exercise 3

1. Prove that if the numbers 1, 2, 3, $\cdots$, n^3 are arranged to form a magic cube then the magic constant S is given by $S = n(n^3 + 1)/2$.

2. Show that in a cube there are exactly 4 three-dimensional diagonals, *i.e.* diagonals which join pairs of vertices, but which do not lie in any face.

3. Prove that in a magic cube of nth order, for which the magic constant S is given, the number of unknowns is n^3, and the number of equations that must be satisfied is $3n^2 + 4$.

4. The Franklin square uses each of the numbers from 1 to 256 just once ($16^2 = 256$). Prove that under these circumstances the magic constant S must be 2056.

5. Although Franklin did not make the claim, his

square is still magic if it is considered on a cylinder with side XY joined to side ZW (Figure 3.21). If we regard the 256 entries as unknown, then the conditions on the rows, columns, and broken diagonals become equations in these unknowns. Using the cylinder, how many such equations are there in the 256 unknowns?

6. Although Franklin made no such claim, his square is also magic on another set of broken diagonals, namely those which on reading from left to right first descend 8 squares and then ascend again, for example $200 + 39 + 230 + \cdots + 204 + 181 + 86 + \cdots + 90 + 185 = 2056$. How many additional equations in the unknowns does this type of broken diagonal give?

7. The Franklin square has the property that if a card, made by cutting a 4×4 hole, is placed anywhere on the square allowing 16 numbers to show through then the sum of these numbers is the magic constant. This is also true on the cylinder obtained by joining the edge XY to the edge ZW. How many additional equations in the unknowns does this condition give?

8. If a 2×8 hole is cut in a card and the card placed anywhere on the square (considered as a cylinder) then the sum of the 16 numbers which show through is again 2056, whether the long side or the short side is horizontal. How many additional equations in the unknowns does this condition give?

9. The Franklin square has another interesting property. If a card with a 2×2 hole is placed anywhere on the square (considered as a cylinder) then the sum of the 4 numbers which show through is 514. Notice this is one-fourth of the magic constant. How many equations in the unknowns does this give?

10. The answers to problems 7 and 8 give a total of 592, so here alone we already have more equations then the 256 unknowns. But if we consider the equations that arise in problem 9, then these 592 equations are all redundant. This means that if the equations given by the conditions of problem 9 are satisfied, then the equations of problem 7 and problem 8 must also be satisfied. Prove this last statement.

CHAPTER 4

Inequalities

1. Introduction. Algebra is usually devoted to the study of "equalities". An equation is just a statement that two quantities are equal. For example $A(B + C) = AB + AC$ asserts that the left side $A(B + C)$ is always the same as the right side $AB + AC$, no matter what numbers are used for A, B, and C provided only that we use the same numbers on both sides. An equation may sometimes be a question "when are the quantities equal?" Thus $x^2 = 3x + 4$, is not an equation for all values of x. Instead it poses the question, find those numbers which when used for x really make the left side equal to the right side. It is the task of algebra to provide tools for a systematic study of such questions. Using algebra it is easy to prove that $x^2 = 3x + 4$ is a true equality if $x = -1$, or if $x = 4$, and for no other values of x.

Similarly there is a systematic method for handling inequalities. This method is designed to tell us when two given quantities are not equal. But it does more: it is a method for telling which of these two quantities is the larger and which is the smaller. This theory of inequalities is of great importance in mathematics, and in the various applications of mathematics to the sciences. Furthermore, the theory is quite attractive and interesting and is well worth studying just for the pleasure it gives.

2. The elementary theorems. The student has already met with a few simple inequalities in Chapters 2 and 3. Here we give a systematic study of inequalities.

If c is a positive number we write

$$0 < c \qquad \text{(read ''zero is less than } c\text{'')}$$

or with the same meaning,

$$c > 0 \qquad \text{(read ''}c\text{ is greater than zero'').}$$

If c is a negative number we write

$$c < 0 \qquad \text{(read ''}c\text{ is less than zero'')}$$

or if we wish

$$0 > c \qquad \text{(read ''zero is greater than } c\text{'').}$$

Examples. $0 < 3$, $-5 < 0$, $1/10 > 0$, $0 > -.000001$.

The comparison of any two numbers is then made to depend on the above basic inequalities.

Definition 1. *The number a is said to be less than b, in symbols*

$$(1) \qquad\qquad a < b \qquad \text{(read ''}a\text{ is less than }b\text{'')}$$

if and only if the difference $b - a$ is positive, i.e. if and only if

$$(2) \qquad\qquad 0 < b - a.$$

If $a < b$ (a is less than b) we also write $b > a$ (b is greater than a). For example $86 < 99$ because $99 - 86 = 13$ a positive number. For the same reason $99 > 86$. Again $-19 < -6$ because $-6 - (-19) = -6 + 19 = 13$ a positive number.

It is convenient to have at hand a compound symbol $\leqq$. Thus the symbols $a \leqq b$ (read ''a is less than or equal to b'') means that either a is less than b, or a is equal to b.

Using the simplest laws of arithmetic we can prove a number of basic theorems on inequalities.

Theorem 1. *If $a < b$ and c is any positive number, then $ca < cb$.*

In other words, an inequality remains valid when multiplied on both sides by the same positive number.

Proof. Since $a < b$, then $b - a$ is a positive number. Since the product of two positive numbers is again positive we have $c(b - a) > 0$. But then

$$0 < c(b - a) = cb - ca$$

and by definition 1 this gives

$$ca < cb. \qquad\qquad \text{Q.E.D.}$$

We leave to the student the proof of

Theorem 2. *If $a < b$ and c is any negative number, then $ca > cb$.*

In other words, when an inequality is multiplied on both sides by the same negative number, the inequality sign is reversed.

Theorem 3. *If $a < b$ and $b < c$, then $a < c$.*

Proof. By hypothesis $b - a$ and $c - b$ are positive numbers. Then the sum $(b - a) + (c - b)$ is a positive number. But this sum is $c - a$. Since $0 < c - a$, we have by definition 1 that $a < c$.

By a similar type of argument the student can prove

Theorem 4. *If $a < c$ and $b < d$, then $a + b < c + d$.*

In other words two inequalities can be added termwise to give a valid inequality. Of course the inequality sign must be in the same direction in all three of the inequalities.

Theorem 5. *If $a < b$ and c is any number, then*

$$a + c < b + c.$$

An inequality remains valid when the same number is added to both sides. We leave the proof for the student. Note that c can be a negative number, so that this theorem includes subtraction.

Theorem 6. *If $0 < a < b$, then*

$$\frac{1}{a} > \frac{1}{b} > 0.$$

Thus reciprocation reverses the inequality sign, when both members are positive.

Proof. Multiply both sides of $a < b$ by the positive number $1/ab$ and use Theorem 1.

Theorem 7. *If $0 < a < b$ and $0 < c < d$ then $ac < bd$.*

Thus multiplication of the corresponding terms of an inequality preserves the inequality. Of course all terms should be positive, and the inequality sign must be in the same direction in all three inequalities.

Proof. Using theorem 1 the inequality $a < b$ yields $ac < bc$. Similarly $c < d$ yields $bc < bd$. Since $ac < bc$ and $bc < bd$, theorem 3 gives $ac < bd$.

Theorem 8. *If $0 < a < b$ and n is any positive integer then*

$$a^n < b^n.$$

Proof. Apply theorem 7, n times with $c = a$, and $d = b$.

Theorem 9. *If $0 < a < b$ and n is any positive integer then*

$$\sqrt[n]{a} < \sqrt[n]{b}.$$

Here if n is even, the symbol $\sqrt[n]{}$ means the positive nth root.

Proof. The proof is a little complicated because it uses the method of contradiction. We contend that for any positive numbers $\sqrt[n]{a}$ and $\sqrt[n]{b}$ there are only three possibilities, namely:

(A) $\sqrt[n]{a} < \sqrt[n]{b}$,   (B) $\sqrt[n]{a} = \sqrt[n]{b}$,   (C) $\sqrt[n]{a} > \sqrt[n]{b}$.

In each of the latter two cases we take the nth power of both sides. In case (B) we find obviously that $a = b$. But this is impossible because by hypothesis $a < b$. In case (C) we apply theorem 8 to $\sqrt[n]{b} < \sqrt[n]{a}$ and find that $b < a$. Again this is contrary to the hypothesis that $a < b$. Since each of the cases (B) and (C) leads to a contradiction, the only case that can occur is (A).   Q.E.D.

There is one other important tool in proving inequalities, namely the innocent remark that the square of any number is either positive or zero, *i.e.* $c^2 \geqq 0$ for any[1] number c.

---

[1] The student may have heard that the imaginary number $i = \sqrt{-1}$ has the property that $i^2 = -1 < 0$. In this book we consider only real numbers.

Example 1. Prove that for any two numbers

$$(3) \qquad 2ab \leqq a^2 + b^2,$$

and that the equality sign occurs if and only if $a = b$.

Solution. By our remark above

$$(4) \qquad (a - b)^2 \geqq 0$$

and equality in (4) occurs if and only if $a = b$. Expanding (4) we have

$$a^2 - 2ab + b^2 \geqq 0,$$

or

$$0 \leqq a^2 - 2ab + b^2.$$

Then by Theorem 5 (adding $2ab$ to both sides)

$$2ab \leqq a^2 + b^2.$$

Since the equality sign occurs in (4) if and only if $a = b$, it also occurs in (3) under the same conditions.

Example 2. Prove that if a, b, c, and d are any set of positive numbers,

$$(5) \qquad ab + cd \leqq \sqrt{a^2 + c^2} \sqrt{b^2 + d^2}.$$

It is not easy to see the proper starting place for this problem, so instead we work backwards. That is, we start with the inequality (5) and see if we can deduce one that we know to be valid. This operation is called the analysis of the problem.

Analysis. If (5) is true we can square both sides and obtain

$$(6) \quad a^2b^2 + 2abcd + c^2d^2 \leqq (a^2 + c^2)(b^2 + d^2),$$

or

$$(7) \quad a^2b^2 + 2abcd + c^2d^2 \leqq a^2b^2 + c^2b^2 + a^2d^2 + c^2d^2,$$

or on transposing (theorem 5)

$$(8) \qquad 0 \leqq c^2b^2 - 2abcd + a^2d^2,$$

or

$$(9) \qquad 0 \leqq (cb - ad)^2.$$

But we know that this last inequality is always valid. Hence if we can reverse our steps we can prove the given inequality is also valid.

Solution. We begin with the known inequality (9) and on expanding we find that (8) is also valid. Then adding $a^2b^2 + 2abcd + c^2d^2$ to both sides of (8) we obtain (7). Factoring the right side of (7) gives (6). Finally taking the positive square root of both sides of (6) gives (5).

Q.E.D.

It is customary to do the analysis on scratch paper, and then write the solution in the proper order, *i.e.* in the reverse order of the analysis. The student should write out in detail the correct solution of this example, following the outline just given.

Some inequalities are valid only for certain values of the variables involved.

Example 3. For what values of x is

$$(10) \qquad x^2 - x - 30 > 0?$$

Solution. Factoring this expression we have

$$(11) \qquad x^2 - x - 30 = (x - 6)(x + 5).$$

This is certainly positive if both factors are positive. This happens only if $x > 6$. The product is also positive if both factors are negative. This happens only for $x < -5$. If $-5 < x$ and $x < 6$, the first factor is negative and the second factor is positive so that the product is negative.

Whence we conclude that the inequality (10) is valid if either $x < -5$ or if $x > 6$, and that these are the only values of x for which (10) is valid.

Example 4. Prove that

$$(12) \qquad \sqrt{2} + \sqrt{6} < \sqrt{3} + \sqrt{5}.$$

Solution. We give the analysis. Squaring both sides of (12) yields

$$(13) \qquad 2 + 2\sqrt{2}\sqrt{6} + 6 < 3 + 2\sqrt{3}\sqrt{5} + 5,$$

or on subtracting 8 from both sides and dividing by 2,

$$(14) \qquad \sqrt{12} < \sqrt{15}.$$

But since $12 < 15$, the inequality (14) is obviously valid (theorem 9). To prove the inequality (12) we start with the remark that $12 < 15$ and reverse the above steps.

Exercise 1

In problems 1 through 12, prove the given inequality under the assumption that all of the variables involved are positive. Determine the conditions under which the equality sign occurs.

1. $a + \dfrac{1}{a} \geqq 2.$

2. $\dfrac{a}{5b} + \dfrac{5b}{4a} \geqq 1.$

3. $\sqrt{\dfrac{c}{d}} + \sqrt{\dfrac{d}{c}} \geqq 2.$

4. $(c + d)^2 \geqq 4cd.$

★5. $\dfrac{a + b}{2} \geqq \sqrt{ab} \geqq \dfrac{2ab}{a + b}.$

6. $(a + 5b)(a + 2b) \geqq 9b(a + b).$

7. $x^2 + 4y^2 \geqq 4xy.$

8. $x^2 + y^2 + z^2 \geqq xy + yz + zx.$

★9. $\dfrac{c^2}{d^2} + \dfrac{d^2}{c^2} + 6 \geqq \dfrac{4c}{d} + \dfrac{4d}{c}.$

10. $\dfrac{a + 3b}{3b} \geqq \dfrac{4a}{a + 3b}.$

★11. $cd(c + d) \leqq c^3 + d^3.$

★12. $4ABCD \leqq (AB + CD)(AC + BD).$

13. Which of the above inequalities are still meaningful and valid if the variables are permitted to assume negative values also?

In problems 14 through 17 determine which of the two given quantities is the larger without using tables.

14. $\sqrt{19} + \sqrt{21}, \quad \sqrt{17} + \sqrt{23}.$

15. $\sqrt{11} - \sqrt{8}, \quad \sqrt{17} - \sqrt{15}.$

16. $\sqrt{17} + 4\sqrt{5}, \quad 5\sqrt{7}.$

17. $2\sqrt{2}$, $\sqrt[3]{23}$.

18. Prove that if $1 < k < n$, then
$$\sqrt{n-k} + \sqrt{n+k} < \sqrt{n-1} + \sqrt{n+1}.$$

19. Prove that the inequality of example 2 (equation (5)) is valid even if some or all of the variables a, b, c, d are negative.

In problems 20 through 25 find the values of x for which the given inequality is valid.

20. $10x - 15 < 7(x - 3)$.
21. $2x - 19 < 11(x - 2)$.
22. $x(x - 1) > 0$.
23. $(x - 8)(x - 1) < 0$.
24. $x^2 - 8x + 24 < 9$.
25. $4x^2 - 13x + 4 < 1$.

26. Prove that if $a < b$, then $a < \dfrac{a+b}{2} < b$.

★3. Some more complicated inequalities. An inequality may involve n variables, where n is an arbitrary positive integer. The positive integer n may also enter in some other natural way. In such cases a proof by mathematical induction may be most suitable.

Example 1. If $a_1, a_2, \cdots, a_n$ are positive numbers each less than one, prove that

$$(15) \quad 1 - (a_1 + a_2 + a_3 + \cdots + a_n)$$
$$\leqq (1 - a_1)(1 - a_2)(1 - a_3) \cdots (1 - a_n).$$

Solution. For $n = 1$, the inequality (15) becomes $1 - a_1 \leqq 1 - a_1$, and this is certainly the case.

Next suppose that (15) is valid for index n and multiply both sides by the positive quantity $(1 - a_{n+1})$. The manipulations will be considerably simplified if we introduce a single letter s_n for the sum on the left, i.e. let

$$s_n = a_1 + a_2 + \cdots + a_n.$$

Then (15) can be written as

$$(16) \quad 1 - s_n \leqq (1 - a_1)(1 - a_2)(1 - a_3) \cdots (1 - a_n).$$

We now assume that (16) is true, and multiply both sides of (16) by the positive number $(1 - a_{n+1})$. This yields

(17) $(1 - s_n)(1 - a_{n+1}) \leqq (1 - a_1)(1 - a_2) \cdots$
$$(1 - a_n)(1 - a_{n+1}).$$

But for the left side of (17) we have

$$(1 - s_n)(1 - a_{n+1}) = 1 - s_n - a_{n+1} + s_n a_{n+1}$$
$$\geqq 1 - s_n - a_{n+1} = 1 - s_{n+1}$$

since $s_n a_{n+1}$ is positive, and since $s_n + a_{n+1} = s_{n+1}$. Using this in (17) gives

$$1 - s_{n+1} \leqq (1 - a_1)(1 - a_2) \cdots (1 - a_n)(1 - a_{n+1})$$

and this is (15) for the index $n + 1$. Hence by the principle of mathematical induction (15) is true for each positive integer n. Q.E.D.

Example 2. Prove that if a and b are positive and if n is any positive integer, then

(18) $$(a + b)^n \leqq 2^{n-1}(a^n + b^n).$$

Solution. For $n = 1$, the inequality (18) becomes $a + b \leqq a + b$ and this is certainly the case.

Next suppose that (18) is valid for index n, and multiply on both sides by the positive quantity $a + b$, obtaining

(19) $(a + b)^{n+1} \leqq 2^{n-1}(a^n + b^n)(a + b)$
$$\leqq 2^{n-1}(a^{n+1} + b^{n+1} + a^n b + ab^n).$$

The first two terms in the right parentheses are in satisfactory form. We should like to replace the last two terms $a^n b + ab^n$ by $a^{n+1} + b^{n+1}$ provided that these latter terms are larger. In other words we need to prove that

(20) $$a^n b + ab^n \leqq a^{n+1} + b^{n+1}.$$

But if we consider the product $(a^n - b^n)(a - b)$ we see that if $a > b$ both terms are positive, and if $a < b$ both terms are negative. Thus in all cases

(21) $$(a^n - b^n)(a - b) \geqq 0.$$

But expanding (21) and transposing gives (20). Using (20) in (19) yields

$$(a+b)^{n+1} \leqq 2^{n-1}(a^{n+1} + b^{n+1} + a^{n+1} + b^{n+1})$$
$$\leqq 2^{n-1}2(a^{n+1} + b^{n+1}) = 2^n(a^{n+1} + b^{n+1}).$$

But this is (18) when the index is $n + 1$.   Q.E.D.

The student is invited to reconsider these two examples and to determine those cases in which the equality sign holds.

Not all inequalities involving a positive integer n require mathematical induction. The next example illustrates this point.

Example 3. Prove that for $n \geqq 1$,

$$(22) \qquad\qquad (n!)^2 \geqq n^n.$$

Solution. Consider the product $(n - k)(k + 1)$. It is easy to see that

$$(23) \quad (n - k)(k + 1) = nk + n - k(k + 1)$$
$$= k(n - k - 1) + n \geqq n,$$

if $n - k - 1 \geqq 0$. In (23) we now put $k = 0, 1, 2, 3, \cdots,$ $n - 1$. We find that

$$n \cdot 1 \geqq n, \quad (n - 1)2 \geqq n, \quad (n - 2)3 \geqq n, \cdots, \quad 1 \cdot n \geqq n,$$

with equality holding only for the first and last of these n equations. If we multiply all of the inequalities of this set together it is obvious that we obtain (22). The equality sign occurs only if $n = 1$, or $n = 2$. The student should try to use mathematical induction on this problem. He will find that this problem is much harder to solve by induction.

★4. **The arithmetic and geometric means.** If we are given n positive numbers $a_1, a_2, \cdots, a_n$ then by definition the *arithmetic* mean A of these numbers is given by

$$(24) \qquad\qquad A = \frac{a_1 + a_2 + \cdots + a_n}{n},$$

and the *geometric mean* G is given by

$$(25) \qquad\qquad G = \sqrt[n]{a_1 a_2 a_3 \cdots a_n}.$$

Theorem 10. *For any n positive numbers*

$$A \geqq G$$

and the equality sign holds if and only if the numbers are all equal.

The proof of this important result requires a preliminary result that is in itself almost obvious.

Theorem 11. *Let m be the smallest number in the set $a_1, a_2, \cdots, a_n$ and let M be the largest number in the set. Then*

$$(26) \qquad m \leqq \frac{a_1 + a_2 + \cdots + a_n}{n} \leqq M$$

with equality if and only if all of the numbers are equal.

Proof of theorem 11. By hypothesis

$$m \leqq a_1 \leqq M,$$
$$m \leqq a_2 \leqq M,$$
$$\vdots$$
$$m \leqq a_n \leqq M.$$

Adding these n inequalities gives

$$(27) \qquad nm \leqq a_1 + a_2 + \cdots + a_n \leqq nM.$$

Dividing (27) by n yields (26). Q.E.D.

Proof of theorem 10. We first remark that if all of the numbers are equal to a then $A = G = a$. Whence we may suppose that the numbers are not all equal. We select the subscripts so that a_1 is the smallest and a_2 is the largest. Then by theorem 11

$$(28) \qquad a_1 < A < a_2.$$

We now consider a new set of positive numbers obtained from the original numbers by replacing the a_1 and a_2 with A and $a_1 + a_2 - A$. The arithmetic mean for this new set is exactly the same as for the original set since

$$\frac{A + (a_1 + a_2 - A) + a_3 + a_4 + \cdots + a_n}{n}$$
$$= \frac{a_1 + a_2 + a_3 + a_4 + \cdots + a_n}{n} = A.$$

How about the geometric mean for the new set? We want to prove that

$$(29) \qquad A(a_1 + a_2 - A) > a_1 a_2,$$

and if this is so then the geometric mean for the new set is larger than for the original set. But (29) is equivalent to

$$Aa_1 + Aa_2 - A^2 - a_1 a_2 > 0$$
$$(30) \qquad (A - a_1)(a_2 - A) > 0.$$

But (30) is the product of two positive numbers by virtue of (28) and consequently is positive. Thus (29) is also valid. Then if G_1 denotes the geometric mean of the new set, we have

$$(31) \quad G_1 = \sqrt[n]{A(a_1 + a_2 - A)a_3 a_4 \cdots a_n}$$
$$> \sqrt[n]{a_1 a_2 a_3 a_4 \cdots a_n} = G$$

so that the geometric mean has increased while the arithmetic mean has remained unchanged. If we repeat this replacement an appropriate number of times, we find that at the end of a *finite* number of steps, the set of numbers is just $A, A, A, \cdots, A$ and the arithmetic mean and the geometric mean are both equal to A. Let $G, G_1, G_2, \cdots, G_k$ be the sequence of geometric means for these sets. Since at each step the geometric mean increases we have

$$G < G_1 < G_2 < \cdots < G_k = A. \qquad \text{Q.E.D.}$$

Example 1. Prove that for any four positive numbers a, b, c, d

$$a^3 b + b^3 c + c^3 d + d^3 a \geqq 4abcd.$$

Solution. If we examine the arithmetic and geometric means of the four quantities on the left, we have (by theorem 10) that

$$\frac{a^3 b + b^3 c + c^3 d + d^3 a}{4} \geqq \sqrt[4]{a^3 b b^3 c c^3 d d^3 a} = abcd. \quad \text{Q.E.D.}$$

Exercise 2

In all of the following problems assume that all of the

variables are positive and that n is a positive integer, unless otherwise noted.

★1. Prove that $(a + b)^2 a^{n-1} b^{n-1} \leqq (a^n + b^n)^2$.

2. Prove that for $n > 1$

$$\frac{1}{\sqrt{1}} + \frac{1}{\sqrt{2}} + \frac{1}{\sqrt{3}} + \cdots + \frac{1}{\sqrt{n}} > \sqrt{n}.$$

3. Prove that if $a_1 < a_2 < \cdots < a_n$, then

$$a_1 < \frac{w_1 a_1 + w_2 a_2 + w_3 a_3 + \cdots + w_n a_n}{w_1 + w_2 + w_3 + \cdots + w_n} < a_n.$$

This generalizes theorem 11.

4. If

$$\frac{a_1}{b_1} < \frac{a_2}{b_2} < \frac{a_3}{b_3} < \cdots < \frac{a_n}{b_n} \qquad \text{prove that}$$

$$\frac{a_1}{b_1} < \frac{a_1 + a_2 + a_3 + \cdots + a_n}{b_1 + b_2 + b_3 + \cdots + b_n} < \frac{a_n}{b_n}.$$

Hint: Use problem 3 and select the weights w_k properly.

5. Prove that

$$5abcde \leqq a^2 b^3 + b^2 c^3 + c^2 d^3 + d^2 e^3 + e^2 a^3.$$

6. Prove that

$$\frac{a_1}{a_2} + \frac{a_2}{a_3} + \frac{a_3}{a_4} + \cdots + \frac{a_{n-1}}{a_n} + \frac{a_n}{a_1} \geqq n.$$

7. Prove that

$$(a_1 + a_2 + \cdots + a_n)\left(\frac{1}{a_1} + \frac{1}{a_2} + \cdots + \frac{1}{a_n}\right) \geqq n^2.$$

★8. Prove that

$$1 + x + x^2 + \cdots + x^{2n} \geqq (2n + 1)x^n.$$

★9. If $a_1, a_2, \cdots, a_n$ are positive numbers each less than one, then

$$(1 - a_1)(1 - a_2)(1 - a_3) \cdots (1 - a_n)$$
$$< \frac{1}{1 + a_1 + a_2 + \cdots + a_n}.$$

Notice that inequality (15) (example 1 of § 3) gives a lower bound for the expression on the left. This problem provides an upper bound for the same quantity. These two inequalities are known as the Weierstrass inequalities.

★10. If a, b, c, and d are greater than 1 prove that

$$8(abcd + 1) > (a + 1)(b + 1)(c + 1)(d + 1).$$

Hint: $2(ab + 1) > (a + 1)(b + 1)$.

★11. $a + b + c \leqq \dfrac{a^2 + b^2}{a + b} + \dfrac{b^2 + c^2}{b + c} + \dfrac{c^2 + a^2}{c + a}.$

12. Prove that
$$(a + b - c)^2 + (b + c - a)^2 + (c + a - b)^2$$
$$\geqq ab + bc + ca.$$

Hint: Use Problem 8 of Exercise 1.

13. $6abc \leqq ab(a + b) + bc(b + c) + ca(c + a).$

★14. Prove that if $n > 1$, then
$$\frac{4^n}{n + 1} < \frac{(2n)!}{(n!)^2}.$$

CHAPTER 5

Mathematical Induction in Geometry

1. Some simple examples. In Chapter 2, we explained the principle of mathematical induction, but all of the examples in that chapter referred to algebra. However, the principle of mathematical induction can be applied to problems in geometry.

Example 1. Prove that n distinct lines all passing through a common point divide the plane into $2n$ regions (parts).

Solution. It is obvious that one line divides the plane into two half-planes and hence the assertion is true when $n = 1$.

Next we assume that the assertion is true when the index n is k, that is we assume that k lines all passing through a point O divide the plane into $2k$ sectors[1] each with vertex at O (see Figure 5.1). If now a new line L is introduced

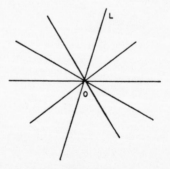

Fig. 5.1

[1]A sector is a region with a special shape, namely it is the region that is enclosed by two rays issuing from a common point.

passing through O, it will lie in exactly two of these sectors, and it will divide each of these sectors into two new sectors, thus adding two more sectors. Then the total number of sectors will be $2k + 2 = 2(k + 1)$. But this is the assertion when the index n is $k + 1$. Q.E.D.

The situation is more complicated if the lines do not all pass through a common point. We say that n lines are *in general position* if no three of the lines have a common intersection point, and no two of the lines are parallel.

Example 2. Prove that n lines in general position divide the plane into $(n^2 + n + 2)/2$ regions. How many of these regions are unbounded (extend to infinity)?

Solution. When $n = 1$, there are 2 such regions, both of which are unbounded, and when $n = 2$, there are 4 such regions, all unbounded. But when $n = 3$, the number of regions is 7, and only six of them are unbounded (see Figure 5.2).

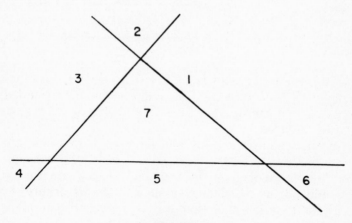

Fig. 5.2

On the other hand the formula $(n^2 + n + 2)/2$ gives in these cases: $(1 + 1 + 2)/2 = 2$, $(4 + 2 + 2)/2 = 4$, and $(9 + 3 + 2)/2 = 7$ respectively. Thus the formula $(n^2 + n + 2)/2$ gives the correct result when $n = 1$, when $n = 2$, and when $n = 3$. Of course logically it was only necessary to check the formula for $n = 1$.

We now assume that k lines in general position divide the plane into $(k^2 + k + 2)/2$ regions. When a new line is introduced, in general position it will intersect each of the k lines once, forming a set of k points on this line, which divides this new line into $k + 1$ parts, or segments. Of these segments, two will be rays (segments extending to infinity in one direction) and the remaining $k - 1$ segments will be finite in length. (If this assertion is not obvious, it can be proved by mathematical induction.) Each of these new $k + 1$ segments acts as a cut dividing a region of the original subdivision into two new regions. In this way the number of regions is increased by $k + 1$, by the addition of the $(k + 1)$th line. Hence the total number of regions is

$$
\begin{aligned}
\frac{k^2 + k + 2}{2} + k + 1 &= \frac{k^2 + k + 2 + 2k + 2}{2} \\
&= \frac{(k^2 + 2k + 1) + (k + 1) + 2}{2} \\
&= \frac{(k + 1)^2 + (k + 1) + 2}{2},
\end{aligned}
$$

and this is the formula when $n = k + 1$. We leave it to the student to prove that $2n$ of the regions will be unbounded, and hence by subtraction $(n - 1)(n - 2)/2$ of the regions will be bounded.

In this example it was relatively easy to prove the formula $(n^2 + n + 2)/2$ once we are given this formula. But how do we discover this formula? In this case it is not too difficult, as we shall now show. Let us denote[2] by $F(n)$ the function of n that we are trying to determine. Since one line divides the plane into 2 regions we have $F(1) = 2$. Further our induction argument showed that adding a line to a set of k lines gives $k + 1$ new regions, so that $F(k)$ is increased by $k + 1$ to give $F(k + 1)$, or

(1) $$F(k + 1) = F(k) + k + 1.$$

[2]The symbol $F(n)$ is read "F of n." See Chapter 1 §6 for a detailed discussion of function notation.

We now set $k = 1, 2, 3, \cdots, n - 1$ in equation (1), obtaining the set of equations

$$F(2) = F(1) + 2,$$
$$F(3) = F(2) + 3,$$
$$F(4) = F(3) + 4,$$
$$\cdot$$
$$\cdot$$
$$\cdot$$
$$\underline{F(n) = F(n - 1) + n.}$$

Adding all of these equations we obtain

$$F(2) + F(3) + \cdots + F(n) = F(1) + F(2) + F(3) + \cdots + F(n - 1) + (2 + 3 + 4 + \cdots + n).$$

The terms $F(2) + F(3) + \cdots + F(n - 1)$ cancel on both sides, giving

$$(2) \qquad F(n) = F(1) + (2 + 3 + 4 + \cdots + n).$$

In problem 3 of exercise 1 in Chapter 2 we learned that

$$(3) \qquad 1 + 2 + 3 + \cdots + n = \frac{n(n + 1)}{2}.$$

We subtract 1 from both sides of equation (3) and substitute the result in (2). We also use the fact that $F(1) = 2$. Then equation (2) becomes

$$F(n) = 2 + \frac{n(n + 1)}{2} - 1 = \frac{n(n + 1)}{2} + 1 = \frac{n^2 + n + 2}{2}.$$

$$\text{Q.E.D.}$$

Exercise 1

1. Prove the assertion about n points on a line contained in the proof of example 2.

2. Prove that n planes, all passing through a common point and such that no three of them intersect in a common line, divide space into $n(n - 1) + 2$ regions. *Hint*: use the result of example 1.

★3. Let n lines be such that k of the lines have a single common intersection point, while no other set of three lines have a common point, and no pair of lines are parallel. Prove that for $n > k$, these lines divide the plane into $(n^2 + n + 3k - k^2)/2$ regions.

4. By selecting an appropriate value of k, use the expression of the preceding problem to obtain the formula $(n^2 + n + 2)/2$ of example 2.

★5. Given a set of circles in the plane such that every pair of circles intersects in two distinct points, prove that these circles divide the plane into $n^2 - n + 2$ regions.

★★6. A set of planes in space is in *general position* if no two of the planes are parallel, no three of the planes intersect in a common line, and no four of the planes intersect in a common point. Prove that n planes in general position divide space into $(n + 1)(n^2 - n + 6)/6$ regions. *Hint*: use the result of example 2.

★★★7. Into how many regions is space divided by n spheres if every pair of them intersects, and no three of them have a common circle of intersection. *Hint*: Consider a sequence of problems: (a) n points dividing a circle, (b) n circles dividing a plane (see problem 5), (c) the given problem.

2. Polygons. A *polygonal path* is a collection of line segments P_1P_2, P_2P_3, P_3P_4, $\cdots$, P_nP_{n+1} joining in turn the points P_1, P_2, P_3, $\cdots$, P_{n+1} (see Figure 5.3). The path is *closed* if the point P_{n+1} coincides with the point P_1. Of

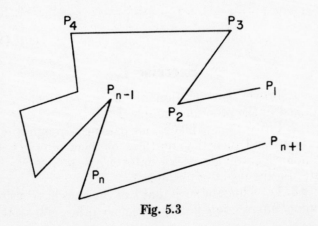

Fig. 5.3

course the path may intersect itself as shown in Figure 5.4. If the closed polygonal path $P_1P_2, P_2P_3, \cdots, P_{n-1}P_n, P_nP_1$ has no self-intersection points (as shown in Figure 5.5)

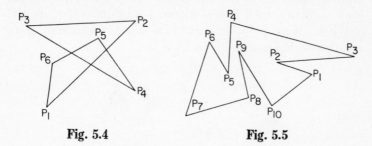

Fig. 5.4   **Fig. 5.5**

then it is called a *simple closed polygonal path*. For brevity such a figure is called a *polygon* and is represented by the symbol $P_1P_2P_3 \cdots P_nP_1$ naming the *vertices* P_1, P_2, $\cdots$, P_n in order. Any line joining two nonadjacent vertices is called a *diagonal*.

A polygon is said to be *convex* if it is the boundary of a convex region. A *region is convex* if given any two points in the region, the line segment joining those two points is also in the region. For example a triangle is convex and a rectangle is also convex. On the other hand the polygons shown in Figures 5.5, 5.6, and 5.7 are not convex.

Before we can use mathematical induction on polygons we need

Theorem 1. *In any polygon with more than 3 sides there is always a diagonal that divides the polygon into two smaller polygons each with fewer sides than the given polygon.*

This may at first seem obvious, for if we refer to the polygon of Figure 5.5, we see that the diagonal P_4P_9 will do. In fact any one of the diagonals P_2P_4, P_2P_9, P_2P_{10}, P_5P_7, P_5P_8, and P_5P_9 also satisfy the requirements of the theorem. But notice that the diagonals P_1P_3, P_4P_6, P_7P_{10}, and P_8P_{10} lie outside the polygon, and that the diagonals such as P_1P_5, P_2P_8 lie partly inside and partly outside the polygon. Is it not possible that for some sufficiently complicated polygon none of the diagonals will lie inside the polygon?

Proof. We consider the interior angle formed by any three successive vertices of the polygon, for example $P_1P_2P_3$. We draw all of the rays that issue from the point P_2 and lie inside the angle $P_1P_2P_3$ and we extend each such ray until it first meets a side (or vertex) of the polygon. Two possible cases can occur, and these cases are shown in Figures 5.6 and 5.7.

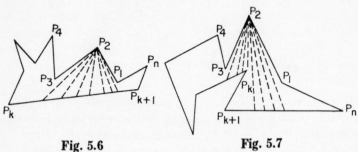

Fig. 5.6   **Fig. 5.7**

Case 1 (Figure 5.6). Suppose that every such ray from P_2 meets the same side of the polygon. In this case the diagonal P_1P_3 will divide the n sided polygon into a triangle $P_1P_2P_3$ and a polygon $P_1P_3P_4 \cdots P_nP_1$ of $n-1$ sides.

Case 2 (Figure 5.7). Suppose that not every ray from P_2 meets the same side, so that at least one ray meets a vertex, say P_k. Then the diagonal P_2P_k divides the n sided polygon into a polygon $P_2P_3 \cdots P_kP_2$ of $k-1$ sides, and a polygon $P_1P_2P_kP_{k+1} \cdots P_nP_1$ of $n-k+3$ sides. But $k \geqq 4$, so this latter polygon has less than n sides.

                                                    Q.E.D.

Example 3. Show that the sum of the interior angles of an n-sided polygon is $(n-2)\ 180°$.

Solution. For a triangle $n = 3$, and it is well known that the sum of the angles of a triangle is $(3-2)\ 180°$. Hence the assertion is true when $n = 3$. It is meaningless when $n = 1$ or 2.

We next assume that the assertion is true for every polygon having k sides *or less* and consider a polygon $P = P_1P_2P_3 \cdots P_{k+1}P_1$ of $k+1$ sides. By theorem 1 there is some diagonal which divides this polygon into two polygons (which we call P_1 and P_2) each having less than $k + 1$ sides. How many sides will these new polygons have? Since the diagonal acts as a side for both P_1 and P_2, and since each of the sides of the old polygon P appears exactly once in just one of the new polygons, it is clear that the total number of sides for both P_1 and P_2 is $k + 3$. Let j be the number of sides for P_1. Consequently the number of sides for P_2 is $k + 3 - j$. But j must be greater than or equal to 3, and hence P_2 has k sides or less. Similarly P_1 has k sides or less. Then we can apply our inductive hypothesis, that our assertion is true for P_1 and P_2. This gives

the sum of the interior angles of $P_1 = (j - 2)180°$,
the sum of the interior angles of $P_2 = (k + 3 - j - 2)180°$.

Therefore: The sum of the interior angles of $P = (k + 1 - 2)180°$.

But this is just our assertion when the index n is $k + 1$.

Q.E.D.

Exercise 2

1. Prove that any polygon of n sides can be divided into $n - 2$ triangles by a set of suitably chosen diagonals.

2. Prove that the number of diagonals used in the disection of problem 1 is $n - 3$.

★3. Prove that in a polygon of n sides the total number of diagonals is $n(n - 3)/2$ if $n \geqq 3$. *Hint*: You can assume that the polygon is convex without loss of generality.

★4. Prove that for any integer $n \geqq 4$ there is a polygon of n sides for which the number of diagonals which lie *outside* the polygon is $(n - 2)(n - 3)/2$.

★5. Show that the number of exterior diagonals obtained in problem 4, is the maximum number of diagonals that can lie outside of an n-sided polygon. *Hint*: Use the results of the first four problems and the fact that

$$\frac{n(n - 3)}{2} = (n - 3) + \frac{(n - 2)(n - 3)}{2}.$$

3. Geographical maps and Euler's Theorem. Suppose

that in the plane we are given a set of points P_1, P_2, $\cdots$, P_n, together with a set of curves that connect some of the points in pairs. (See Figure 5.8.) We assume

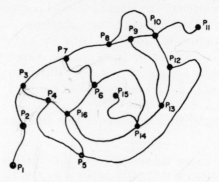

Fig. 5.8

further that no two of the curves intersect, although of course a pair of curves will have a common end point if they both terminate in one of the given points P_k.

We also assume that all of the given points are *connected*, that is we can start at any one of the points P_j and by traversing some of the given curves, arrive at any other point P_k. Such a system of points and curves divides the plane into *regions*.

It is natural to regard the regions as countries, and the curves as boundaries for the countries. The given points P_k are called *vertices*. The entire collection of countries, boundary curves, and vertices is called a *geographical map* (or more briefly, a *map*).

Let V denote the number of vertices, let E (edges) denote the number of boundary curves, and let F (faces) denote the number of countries in a map. Thus for the map shown in Figure 5.8 we have $V = 16$, $E = 22$, and $F = 8$. Observe that in counting the countries we included the outside region (the unbounded one) as a country.

At first glance it may seem that there is no relation between the quantities V, E, and F, but Euler discovered and proved the following very remarkable theorem.

Euler's Theorem. *In any map*

(4) $$V - E + F = 2.$$

Proof. We use mathematical induction on E, the number of boundary curves. However the procedure is complicated by the fact that a number of different cases may occur.

We begin by checking equation (4) in a number of simple cases. If there is only one vertex then there are no curves and just one country, namely the entire plane. In this case we have

$$V - E + F = 1 - 0 + 1 = 2,$$

so equation (4) is valid.

Similarly if we have two vertices joined by a single curve, then again there is only one country and

$$V - E + F = 2 - 1 + 1 = 2.$$

If the two points are joined by a pair of curves (as shown in Figure 5.9) then the map contains two countries and this time equation (4) yields

$$V - E + F = 2 - 2 + 2 = 2.$$

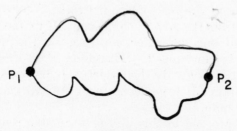

Fig. 5.9

We now turn to the general situation. We suppose that equation (4) holds for all maps in which the number of curves is less than or equal to $E - 1$. Here $E - 1$ plays the role of k. We consider a map M in which there are $E = k + 1$ curves.

Suppose that the given map M contains a vertex in which just two of the curves terminate. This situation is illustrated by the point P_2 of Figure 5.8. In this case we form a new map M' (read "M prime") by suppressing the vertex in question and joining the two curves that terminate at that vertex to form a single curve. Thus in passing from the map M to the map M' we have decreased the number of vertices by 1 and the number of boundaries by 1, while the number of countries is obviously unchanged. If V', E', and F' represent the quantities associated with M' then $V' = V - 1$, $E' = E - 1$, and $F' = F$. By our inductive hypothesis [equation (4)] we have

$$(5) \qquad\qquad V' - E' + F' = 2.$$

Therefore

$$(6) \qquad\qquad (V' + 1) - (E' + 1) + F' = 2$$

and this gives

$$(4) \qquad\qquad V - E + F = 2.$$

Suppose next that M contains a vertex at which only one of the curves terminates. This is illustrated by the points P_1, P_{11} and P_{15} of Figure 5.8. We form a new map M' by suppressing that vertex and the single curve that connects it to the rest of the network of curves. Again in passing from the map M to the map M' we have lost one vertex, and one boundary curve, while the number of countries is unchanged. Therefore $V' = V - 1$, $E' = E - 1$, and $F' = F$. By the inductive hypothesis we again have equation (5) from which we obtain (6) and finally (4) for the map M.

We can proceed in this way step by step removing all of the vertices at which either one or two boundary curves terminate. This procedure will end in one of two ways. Either we will arrive at a map with only one or two vertices of the type already discussed, or we will arrive at a map for which every vertex is a terminal point of three or more curves. In this latter case it is clear that there will be at least two countries, an unbounded one (which is always present) and at least one bounded region.

Let C be a curve which divides the unbounded country

from some adjacent bounded region. (For example the curve P_5P_{12} of Figure 5.8). We form a new map M' by suppressing the curve. In doing so the bounded country is annexed by the unbounded country, so the number of countries is decreased by one. But each vertex is a terminal point for at least three curves, so that the suppression of the curve C does not change the number of vertices. Hence for the new map M' we have $V' = V$, $E' = E - 1$, and $F' = F - 1$. If we assume that for M'

$$V' - E' + F' = 2,$$

then we find that

$$V' - (E' + 1) + (F' + 1) = 2,$$

and this is equivalent to

(4) $$V - E + F = 2.$$

We have shown that any map with $E = k + 1$ edges, can be reduced to a map with $E' = k$ edges. Assuming that $V' - E' + F' = 2$ for any map with k edges, we have proved that $V - E + F = 2$ for any map of $k + 1$ edges. Since the early cases, $k = 0$, $k = 1$, $k = 2$ also yield $V - E + F = 2$, this completes the proof of the theorem.

Exercise 3

In problems 1 through 5 a map is described. In each case find V, E, and F and by direct substitution in $V - E + F = 2$, check that Euler's Theorem is true.

1. A Star of David is formed by placing one equilateral triangle on another one of the same size so that the sides of each triangle trisect the sides of the other.

2. From one vertex of a triangle n line segments are drawn to points on the opposite side, giving a total of $n + 2$ lines from one vertex, and two from each of the other vertices.

3. In a regular n-gon, lines are drawn from the center to each of the vertices.

4. A rectangle is subdivided by p additional line segments parallel and equal to one pair of opposite sides, and q additional line segments parallel and equal to the other pair of opposite sides. All of the line segments lie completely inside the given rectangle except for their end points.

5. With the same center, p circles are drawn with different radii, and then q radial lines are drawn each extending to the largest circle.

6. Is there any change in the formula if the rectangle of problem 4 is a parallelogram?

4. A closer look at Euler's Theorem. This theorem is sufficiently important to deserve a little discussion. It should be observed that in our definition of a map, we required that the network of vertices and curves be connected. What happens to Euler's formula if the configuration is not connected? Let us consider the configuration consisting of three disjoint squares (each exterior to the other two) shown in Figure 5.10. For this configuration

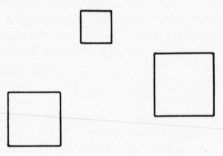

Fig. 5.10

$V = 12$, $E = 12$, and $F = 4$, so that $V - E + F = 12 - 12 + 4 = 4 \neq 2$. Thus if the network of points and curves do not form a connected set, Euler's Theorem is not necessarily valid.

Is Euler's Theorem still valid if the map is drawn on a sphere? The answer is yes, and in fact this is easily proved by using a *stereographic projection*, as we shall now show.

Let us place a sphere so that it is tangent to a plane at a

common point S (Figure 5.11). Let N be the point on the sphere diametrically opposite the point[3] S. Let P be any

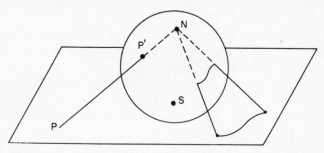

Fig. 5.11

point of the plane and let P' be the point of intersection of the line PN with the sphere. The *stereographic transformation* is the transformation that makes these points P and P' correspond. Thus each point P of the plane goes into a uniquely determined point P' on the sphere under the stereographic projection. Conversely, with the exception of the point N, each point P' on the surface of the sphere corresponds to a unique point P of the plane. If we consider any map M' drawn on the sphere, and select for N a point not a vertex or on a boundary curve of M', then the stereographic projection carries a map M' on the sphere into a map M on the plane, taking vertices into vertices, boundary curves into boundary curves, and countries into countries. Thus any formula relating V, E, and F for a map M on the plane must also be valid for V', E', and F' for the corresponding map M' on the sphere, since $V' = V$, $E' = E$, and $F' = F$.

We have just proved that Euler's Theorem is valid for maps drawn on a sphere. How about other surfaces? Let us consider the torus shown in Figure 5.12. By definition a torus is the surface generated by a circle when the circle is rotated through $360°$ about an axis which lies in the plane of the circle but does not meet the circle. For

---

[3]Here it is convenient to think of S as the South Pole, and N as the North Pole.

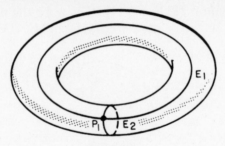

Fig. 5.12

the particular map shown in Figure 5.12, we have $V = 1$, $E = 2$, and $F = 1$, and consequently $V - E + F = 1 - 2 + 1 = 0$. Clearly the formula $V - E + F = 2$ fails on the torus.

5. An application of Euler's Theorem. If a vertex is the terminal point of two boundary curves we call it a vertex of order 2 (or second order). For example the point P_2 in Figure 5.8 is a vertex of second order. Similarly the points P_3, P_4, P_5, and P_6 in Figure 5.8 are vertices of third order. A boundary curve does not always separate two different regions. For example the same region lies on both sides of the curves P_1P_2, P_2P_3, and $P_{10}P_{11}$ of Figure 5.8. The same is true of the curve $P_{14}P_{15}$. All of the other curves of that map have the property that they separate different regions. In any *real* geographical map, every vertex will be of third order or greater, and every curve (border line) will separate two different regions (countries).

Example 1. Let M be a map in which each boundary curve separates different regions, and suppose further that the map has no vertices of first or second order. Prove that for such a map there is always at least one country that has five boundary curves or less.

Solution. If we count the times that a boundary curve meets a vertex it is greater than or equal to $3V$ (three times the number of vertices) since, by hypothesis, 3 or more boundary curves meet at each vertex. But each boundary curve terminates at two vertices (one at each end) so this counting gives $2E$ (twice the number of boundary curves).

Therefore $3V \leqq 2E$ or

$$(7) \qquad\qquad V \leqq \tfrac{2}{3}E.$$

We next suppose that there are no countries with five boundary curves or less. This means that each country has at least six boundary curves, and if we count the occurrences of a boundary curve on a country we have at least $6F$ (six times the number of countries). But each boundary curve separates two different countries (one on each side) and hence is counted twice in the above counting. Therefore $2E \geqq 6F$ or

$$(8) \qquad\qquad F \leqq \tfrac{1}{3}E.$$

Adding equations (7) and (8) yields

$$(9) \qquad\qquad V + F \leqq E.$$

But by Euler's Theorem $V + F = E + 2 > E$. This contradicts (9). Therefore at least one country has five boundaries or less.

Exercise 4

★**1.** Let 5 points be given in the plane. Show that it is impossible to draw the 10 curves joining every possible pair in such a way that no two of the curves intersect.

2. Prove that if every vertex is of third order then the number of vertices is even. Prove that in this case the number of edges is always divisible by 3.

3. A polyhedron is a three-dimensional figure bounded by portions of planes. The polyhedron is said to be convex if given any two points in the polyhedron the line segment joining the two points lies in the polyhedron. Prove that Euler's formula $V - E + F = 2$ applies to a convex polyhedron, where now V is the number of vertices, E is the number of edges, and F is the number of faces of the polyhedron. *Hint*: Place the polyhedron inside a large sphere and project the surface of the polyhedron onto the surface of the sphere from some point inside the polyhedron. This gives a geographical map on a sphere.

4. Find V, E, and F for each of the five regular solids pictured below and by direct substitution check that Euler's formula $V - E + F = 2$, is true.

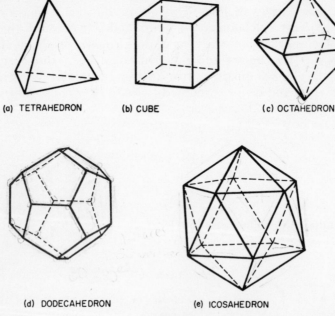

(a) TETRAHEDRON   (b) CUBE   (c) OCTAHEDRON

(d) DODECAHEDRON   (e) ICOSAHEDRON

Fig. 5.13

5. A right pyramid has a regular n-gon for its base. Find V, E, and F and check Euler's formula.

6. Do the same for a right cylinder with a regular n-gon for a base.

★7. In a polyhedron it is obvious that at least three edges meet at each vertex. Further since each face is a polygon with three sides or more, each face is bounded by three edges or more. Following the methods of example 1 it is easy to see that for a polyhedron

$$2E \geqq 3V, \qquad \text{and} \quad 2E \geqq 3F.$$

Use these results and Euler's formula to prove that for a convex polyhedron:

$$2V \geqq F + 4, \quad \text{and} \quad 2F \geqq V + 4,$$

and

$$3V \geqq E + 6, \quad \text{and} \quad 3F \geqq E + 6.$$

Notice that if the symbols V and F, for the number of vertices and faces, are interchanged in the above formulas, we obtain the same set of formulas. Thus the formulas, (and also Euler's formula) are symmetric with respect to V and F.

8. From the inequalities of problem 7 prove that for a convex polyhedron
$$\tfrac{1}{3}E + 2 \leqq V \leqq \tfrac{2}{3}E.$$

9. Use the inequality of problem 8 to prove that there is no convex polyhedron with exactly seven edges.

★★**10.** Prove that for maps drawn on a torus Euler's formula becomes $V - E + F = 0$. *Hint:* The proof goes by induction and runs parallel to the proof given in § 3 for the plane. However the initial map is similar to the map shown in Figure 5.12.

CHAPTER 6

The Four Color Problem

1. Unsolved problems. In our progress through algebra and geometry we observe a skillfully organized body of material of great beauty. Systematic methods are developed for handling problems, and when these methods are properly applied, seemingly difficult problems become quite easy. At first glance, one might expect that this development can be continued indefinitely, and that all mathematics problems can be solved, if only the proper methods are used. But this expectation is far from being realized, and the truth is that there are a large number of problems that have been proposed, and to this day have not been solved despite the best efforts of the greatest mathematicians both past and present. It is a sad fact, but also a fascinating and stimulating fact, for in these problems lies the challenge to future mathematicians to invent more powerful methods.

Most of these unsolved problems require an extensive mathematical background, but a few of them are sufficiently simple that they can be included in this book. Most of these simple ones belong to the domain of number theory and we will mention some of them in Chapter 10. However the four color problem is a nice simple geometry problem that is still unsolved.[1]

[1]Perhaps the reader has heard that no one has yet trisected an arbitrary angle using the straightedge and compass. This is *not* an unsolved problem. It has been solved. The *impossibility* of such a construction has been *proved*, and a proof can be found in almost any book on the Theory of Equations. See for example S. Borofsky, *Elementary Theory of Equations* (New York: The Macmillan Company, 1950).

2. Statement of the problem. Suppose we have a geographical map (see Figure 6.1) that we wish to color. It is quite natural to demand that if two countries have a

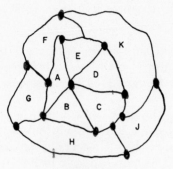

Fig. 6.1

common boundary curve then these two countries should be colored differently. Such is the case with the countries G and H. On the other hand two countries such as A and C may have only a vertex in common. In this case we permit the use of the same color for both countries. We observe that a country must be connected; for example the regions F and H must be regarded as two separate

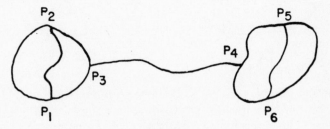

Fig. 6.2

countries, because they are not connected. Finally we observe that the map shown in Figure 6.2 has a boundary curve $P_3 P_4$ that does not separate two countries, since the very same country lies on both sides of this curve. It makes no sense to try to color this map so that the coloring is different on the two sides of this arc. For this reason, such curves will not be allowed, *i.e.* we will consider only those maps with the property that each boundary curve separates two distinct countries.

Definition 1. *A map is said to be properly colored if each country has a definite color and if whenever two countries have a common boundary curve, these two countries have different colors.*

For example, the map shown in Figure 6.1 could be colored properly using ten different colors, one for each of the ten countries. But this would be wasteful, for we could also color this map properly using just four different colors. Let us denote the colors used by the letters *b, g, r,* and *y* (for blue, green, red, and yellow). With this notation a proper coloration for the map is shown in Figure 6.3. Notice that a proper coloration is not necessarily

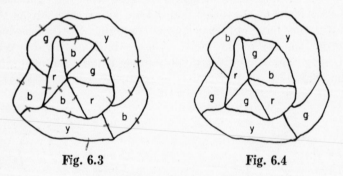

Fig. 6.3   Fig. 6.4

unique. The coloring can be done in many ways and still be proper. Suppose that we have a proper coloring of a map. The interchange of any two of the colors will lead to a different coloring of the map which is also proper. This fact is illustrated by the coloring shown in Figure 6.4, which is obtained from that used in Figure 6.3 by interchanging the colors *b* and *g*.

It is an experimental fact, that every map that has ever been made on the plane or the surface of a sphere can be properly colored using only four colors. But a proof that four colors will always suffice to color properly any such map has not yet been found.

Until such a proof is found, the problem remains open. We just don't know the solution. It is entirely possible that a map can be found that requires five colors for a proper coloration. If such a map is found this would settle the question, for as we will see in § 5 of this chapter, it is possible to prove that five colors are sufficient to color properly any map on the plane.

The four color problem is the problem of proving or disproving the conjecture that four colors are always sufficient to color properly any map on the plane.

3. A brief history of the problem. As far as we know the problem was first mentioned by Möbius[2] in his lectures in 1840. Both Kempe[3] and Tait[4] published "proofs" that four colors are sufficient. Actually Tait merely proved that the four color problem could be solved if one could solve an equally difficult problem on the coloring of graphs. But needless to say, this graph problem is still unsolved to this day. The error in Kempe's proof is more delicate, and in fact for ten years the error went undetected until Heawood[5] pointed out the mistake in Kempe's proof. In this very same paper Heawood proved that five colors are sufficient, and it is this proof that we give in § 5. Further Heawood solved the map-coloring problem on the torus, and we give this solution in § 6. This last result is remarkable, because the torus is a more complicated surface than the plane or sphere, and normally one would expect that the map-coloring problem would be more difficult on the torus.

[2]Alfred F. Möbius, 1790–1868.

[3]A. B. Kempe, "On the Geographical Problem of the Four Colours," *American Journal of Mathematics*, vol. 2 (1879), pp. 193–200.

[4]Peter Guthrie Tait, "Note on a Theorem of Position," *Transactions of the Royal Society of Edinburgh*, vol. 29 (1880), pp. 657–660.

[5]P. J. Heawood, "Map-colour Theorem," *Quarterly Journal of Mathematics*, vol. 24 (1890), pp. 332–338.

The fact that this problem in the plane, now regarded as unsolved, was considered as solved during the years from 1880 to 1890, is rather disquieting. It suggests that perhaps there are today many theorems that we regard as proved, that really have not been proved, because the "proofs" offered contain errors, as yet unnoticed.

Each student of mathematics has a duty to himself to examine each proof as carefully as he can in order to convince himself that the proof is indeed correct.

★4. **A simplification of the problem.** We recall that a vertex is said to be of nth order if n boundary curves meet at this vertex.

Definition 2. *A map is said to be normal if every vertex of the map is a vertex of third order.*

We will prove that in order to solve the four color problem *it is sufficient to solve it just for normal maps.* This does not settle the problem by any means, but it does allow us the luxury of considering just the normal maps. Our task is to prove that if we are given any map M then we can alter it to form a new map M' that is normal and such that if M' can be colored properly with four colors, then the original map M can also be colored properly with four colors.

In this connection let us consider the map M shown in Figure 6.5. All of the vertices of this map are third order

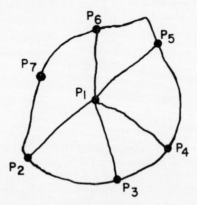

Fig. 6.5

vertices except for P_1 which is of fifth order and P_7 which is of second order.

The vertex P_7 can be eliminated by merely merging the two boundary curves P_2P_7 and P_7P_6 to form one longer boundary curve P_2P_6. Obviously this would not affect the coloring of the countries. Similarly in any map, all of the second order vertices can be eliminated.

To remove the fifth order vertex at P_1, we draw around P_1 a little circle with radius so small that it intersects only those boundary curves that terminate at P_1. We then form a new map M' by adding the territory enclosed by this little circle to one of the original countries. The resulting map is shown in Figure 6.6. In this map all of the

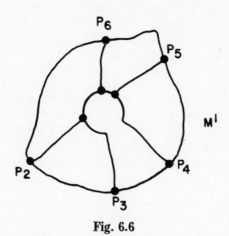

Fig. 6.6

vertices are of third order. If the map of Figure 6.6 can be colored properly with four colors, then the same coloring applied to the map of Figure 6.5 would also give a proper coloring. For whenever two countries in the map of Figure 6.5 have a common boundary curve, the same two countries have a common boundary curve in the map of Figure 6.6.

This procedure is completely general. Figures 6.7 and 6.8 show two maps M and M', where M' is obtained from

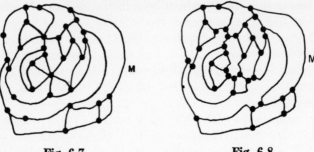

Fig. 6.7   Fig. 6.8

M by eliminating all vertices not of third order by the method just described. The new map M' is a normal map (all vertices are of third order) and any proper coloring of M', leads to a proper coloring of M.

The map of Figure 6.8 does not at first glance look any simpler than that of Figure 6.7. However for normal maps we have the useful

Theorem 1. *In any normal map on the plane or sphere, there is at least one country with five boundary curves or less.*

The proof of this theorem has already been given as the solution to example 1, of § 5 Chapter 5.

★**5. The five color theorem.** This section is devoted to the proof of

Theorem 2. *Any map on the plane or sphere can be colored properly with five colors.*

Proof. As one might suspect, in a difficult problem of this nature we use mathematical induction. By the argument of the preceding section we can assume that the map is normal, and by theorem 1 a normal map always has at least one country with five boundary curves or less. We carry out our induction using for n, the number of countries in the map. The beginning of the induction is trivial, for whenever $n \leqq 5$, it is obvious that five colors will be sufficient.

Now let M be a normal map consisting of $n + 1$ countries. We will destroy one of the countries to form a new normal map M' with only n countries. We select for destruction a country with five boundaries or less. Various cases can occur, according as the country selected has two, three, four, or five boundaries. The first three cases are simple, and the procedure is indicated in parts (a), (b), and (c) of Figure 6.9. In each case the shaded country is

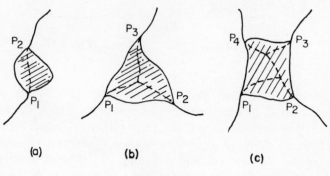

Fig. 6.9

destroyed by deleting the boundary curves between the lettered vertices and introducing the new boundaries shown dotted. The result in each case is a new normal map M' with only n countries. By the inductive hypothesis the map M' can be colored properly using only five colors. We can then restore the country we have destroyed, and since at most it has only four adjacent countries, there is always available for this country a color that has not been used on the adjacent countries. Whence the map M can also be colored properly with only five colors.

The difficult part of the proof occurs in the case that all of the countries of M have five boundary curves or more. We select for our consideration a country C with exactly five boundary curves (by theorem 1, there must be such a country). The situation is illustrated in Figure 6.10 where the areas adjacent to C have been numbered from 1 to 5. Actually two of these areas may belong to one country or to adjacent countries. For example as shown in Figure 6.10, the areas 2 and 4 could belong to

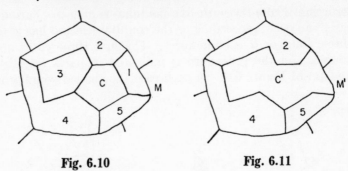

Fig. 6.10   **Fig. 6.11**

adjacent countries. But if this occurs, then the areas 1 and 3 must belong to different countries which have no boundary curve in common. Thus either the areas 2 and 4 belong to different countries with no common boundary curve, or the areas 1 and 3 belong to different countries with no common boundary curve, and in any case there is always at least one such pair. Let us assume that it is the pair 1 and 3 as shown in Figure 6.10. We then form a new map M' by letting the country C annex the countries 1 and 3 forming a new country C'. (See Figure 6.11.) The map M' will be normal and will have only $n-1$ countries. Hence by the inductive hypothesis M' can be colored properly with five colors. We restore the countries 1 and 3 and assign to them the coloring that C' had in M', while leaving C tentatively uncolored. Of course all of the other countries in M are to have the same coloring that they had in M'. Now countries 1 and 3 have the same color, but this is acceptable because they have no common boundary. Thus the countries 1, 2, 3, 4, and 5 surrounding C are colored using only four colors, so that C can now be colored with the color not used on the adjacent countries.   Q.E.D.

★**6. On the torus.** To solve the map coloring problem on the torus we need the analogue of theorem 1, namely

Theorem 3. *In any normal map on the torus, there is at least one country with six boundary curves or less.*

Proof. We have seen in problem 10 of exercise 4, Chapter 5 that Euler's formula on the torus is

$$(1) \qquad V - E + F = 0.$$

Since each vertex is of third order, $3V$ gives a counting of the number of times a boundary curve terminates at a vertex. But this is just twice the number of curves and hence

$$(2) \qquad 3V = 2E.$$

Eliminating V from equation (1) and (2) we find that for a normal map on the torus $E = 3F$, or

$$(3) \qquad 2E = 6F.$$

Now let us assume that every country has seven or more boundary curves. Then a counting of the occurrence of boundary curves for countries yields at least $7F$. But in this counting each boundary curve is counted twice, because each boundary curve separates two different countries. Therefore we have

$$(4) \qquad 2E \geqq 7F.$$

But (3) and (4) are contradictory, and hence there is at least one country with six boundary curves or less.

Theorem 4. *Any map on the torus can be colored properly with seven colors. Further there is a map on the torus which requires seven colors and cannot be colored properly with fewer colors.*

We prove the first part of this theorem by induction on n the number of countries. Let M be a map with $n + 1$ countries. By theorem 3 there is at least one country C with six boundaries or less. We form a new normal map M' with n countries by destroying C. By the inductive hypothesis the map M' can be colored using seven colors. We now restore the country C and since it has at most six neighbors there is always available for C, a color distinct from that used in coloring the countries surrounding C. Since the problem of coloring the countries when $n \leqq 7$ is trivial, this completes the proof of the first part of theorem 4. Thus seven colors are sufficient on a torus.

To prove that seven colors are also necessary we must give an example of a map in which all of the seven colors are needed. This will be the case if each of seven countries touches each of the other six. Now this is actually easy to arrange on the surface of a torus, but it is hard to visualize in a two-dimensional drawing. In order to make the map easy to see, it is convenient to cut the torus as shown in Figure 6.12 along the two circles AXC and AZB. The torus can then be unrolled to form the rectangle shown in Figure 6.13. Perhaps this reduction is easier to visualize

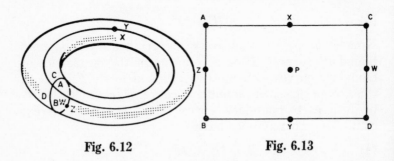

Fig. 6.12   **Fig. 6.13**

if we start with the rectangle of Figure 6.13, and first roll it up joining the edge BYD to AXC to form a cylinder. The cylinder is then bent around and the circular end CWD is joined to the other circular end AZB to form a torus. Thus any map on the surface of the torus can be drawn on the rectangle, if we keep in mind that the points of the line AXC are to be identified with the points of the line BYD, and likewise the line AZB is to be identified with the line CWD. In other words a man starting from P and walking upward to X would (if he were on the torus and continued his trip in the same direction) reappear at Y and continue upward returning to P. With these conventions the points A, B, C, and D at the corners of the rectangle all represent the same point on the torus. Thus a country containing this point would appear in four pieces on the rectangle (this is country number 7 in Figure 6.14).

It is now a simple matter to give an example of a map on the torus that requires seven colors for a proper coloring.

One such map is shown in Figure 6.14, where there are exactly seven countries, each one of which has a common boundary curve with each of the remaining six. Q.E.D.

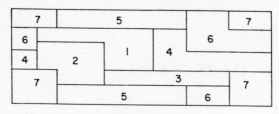

Fig. 6.14

The reader who is interested in digging deeper into this type of mathematics should read the little booklet by L. I. Golovina and I. M. Yaglom, *Induction in Geometry* (Boston: D. C. Heath and Co., 1961), or see the article "Map-coloring Problems," by H. S. M. Coxeter, *Scripta Mathematica*, vol. 23 (1957), pp. 11–25.

CHAPTER 7

The Conic Sections

1. The right circular cone. Let C be some plane curve
and let V be a point not in the plane of C (see Figure 7.1).

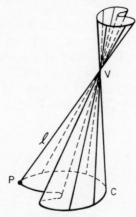

Fig. 7.1

We pass a line l through V and a point P on the curve C,
and then allow the point P to describe the curve C, always
holding the point V fixed. The surface generated by this
moving line is called a *cone*. The point V is called the *vertex*
of the cone, and any one of the lines l which lie in the surface of the cone is called an *element* of the cone.

If the curve C is a circle, then the surface generated by
the line l, is called a *circular cone*.

In particular, if the line y perpendicular to the plane
of the circle at the center of the circle passes through V
then the cone is called a *right circular cone* (see Figure 7.2).
The line y is called the *axis* of the right circular cone.

The right circular cone can be obtained in another way. Let two lines l and y intersect at a point V forming an angle A (Figure 7.3). If the line l is rotated about the fixed line y, always keeping the angle A constant, it is obvious that the line l will generate a right circular cone with vertex V and axis y. The angle A is called the *cone angle*. It follows immediately from this alternate definition that any plane perpendicular to the axis of a right circular cone will cut that cone in a circle. For, referring to Figure 7.2, the distance OP will be constant throughout the rotation.

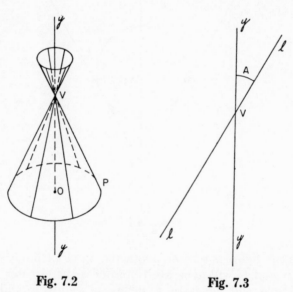

Fig. 7.2   **Fig. 7.3**

Let us imagine temporarily that the cone is made from a sheet of metal, and that a ball is dropped in from the top. It is obvious that the ball will come to rest in such a way that its points of contact with the conical surface form a circle. This is the content of

Theorem 1. *Given a right circular cone and a sphere of radius r, there is a position for the sphere such that its points of tangency with the cone form a circle. Further this circle lies in a plane perpendicular to the axis of the cone.*

Proof. Instead of beginning with the sphere and the cone, we start with a plane containing the axis y of the cone. This plane will cut the cone in two straight lines l_1 and l_2 which make equal angles with the axis. We locate a point O on the line y so that its distance from l_1 is r. Then a circle with center O and radius r will be tangent to the lines l_1 and l_2 at the points P_1 and P_2 (Figure 7.4). If

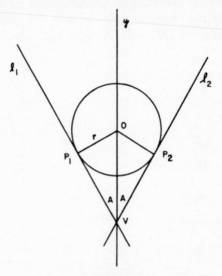

Fig. 7.4

this entire figure is rotated about the line y each one of the lines l_1 and l_2 will generate the same right circular cone. The circle will generate a sphere of radius r and this sphere will be tangent to the cone along the curve generated by the points P_1 and P_2. But this curve is a circle that lies in a plane perpendicular to the line y. Q.E.D.

Theorem 2. *If two line segments PP_1 and PP_2 from a common point P outside a sphere are tangent to the sphere at P_1 and P_2 then they have the same lengths (Figure 7.5).*

Let O be the center of the sphere. Then the two right triangles OP_1P and OP_2P are congruent and hence the corresponding sides P_1P and P_2P are equal. We leave it to the reader to fill in the details.

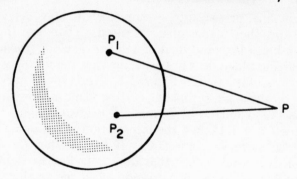

Fig. 7.5

2. The conic sections as sections of a cone. Let us pass a plane through a right circular cone, and consider the figure formed by the intersection, *i.e.* the points that lie on both the plane and the cone. If the plane passes through the vertex V of the cone we may get just a single point, or a

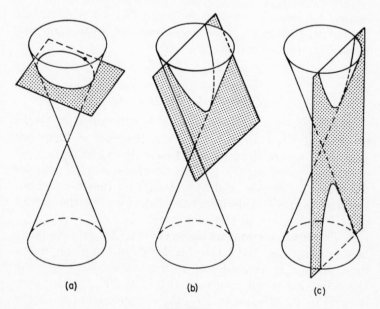

(a) (b) (c)

Fig. 7.6

straight line, or two intersecting straight lines depending upon how the cutting plane is tilted. These are the uninteresting cases and henceforth we exclude them. If the cutting plane does not pass through the vertex we get a curve as illustrated in Figure 7.6. The type of curve depends on the angle B that the cutting plane makes with the axis of the cylinder. If the angle B is greater than A (see Figures 7.3 or 7.4) then the intersection is a simple closed curve, as shown in Figure 7.6a. If $B = A$, then the intersection is a single curve that does not close as shown in Figure 7.6b. This is the situation when the cutting plane is parallel to one of the elements of the cone. If $B < A$ then the intersection is a pair of curves, both of which are, unbounded, as illustrated in Figure 7.6c. It is convenient to call this intersection a single curve, and to regard it as having two pieces. These curves are called the ellipse, parabola, and hyperbola respectively. For convenience we summarize in

Definition 1. *Let P be a plane that makes an angle B with the axis of a right circular cone, and let A be the cone angle. Suppose further that the plane does not pass through the vertex of the cone. Then the intersection of the plane and the cone is a curve that is called*

> (a) *an ellipse if $B > A$,*
> (b) *a parabola if $B = A$,*
> (c) *a hyperbola if $B < A$.*

This definition is the one used by the ancient Greek scholars and it is quite attractive. However it turns out that if we ignore the cone and look only at the plane that contains the curve, there is an alternate way of defining the ellipse, parabola, and hyperbola, and that for computational purposes this alternate definition is the better one. This is given in the next section.

3. The conic sections as plane curves. To define a parabola, we suppose that a line d is drawn in the plane, and a fixed point F is selected, not on the line d. We then take the collection of all points P such that PF, the distance from P to F, is equal to PD, the distance from P to the line d. This collection of points is called a *parabola*, the point F is called its *focus*, and the line d is called its *directrix*. Points on the parabola can be constructed with ruler and compass, and the construction of several such points is shown in Figure 7.7. A portion of the parabola is shown in Figure 7.8.

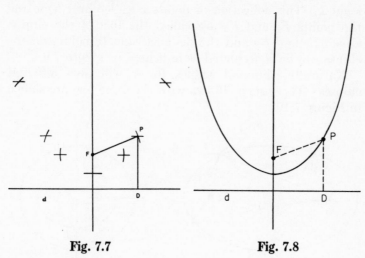

Fig. 7.7   Fig. 7.8

We summarize the above remarks in

Definition 2. *A parabola is a curve formed by the set of all points P such that*

(1) $$PF = PD$$

where PF is the distance of P from a fixed point F, called the focus of the parabola and PD is the distance of P from a fixed line d called the directrix of the parabola.

The line through the focus F and perpendicular to the directrix d is called the *axis* of the parabola. The axis is a line of symmetry for the parabola. This means that if the curve is drawn carefully and the paper is folded along the axis, the two parts of the curve will coincide. The precise mathematical definition is given in

Definition 3. *A line is called an axis of symmetry for a curve, if every chord of the curve that is perpendicular to the line is bisected by the line.*

To define an ellipse we take two fixed points F_1 and F_2 in the plane, and we select a constant k that is larger than the distance between the two points F_1 and F_2. We then take the collection of all points P such that the sum of the distances of P from F_1 and F_2 is always equal to the constant k. This collection of points is called an *ellipse* and the points F_1 and F_2 are called the foci of the ellipse. Given F_1 and F_2 and the distance sum k, points on the ellipse can be constructed as indicated in Figure 7.9.

Naturally, different values for k will give different ellipses. Three such ellipses with the same foci are shown in Figure 7.10.

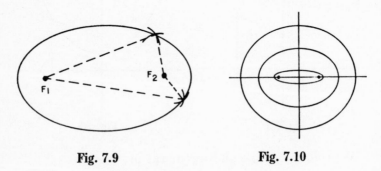

Fig. 7.9   Fig. 7.10

We summarize the above remarks in

Definition 4. *An ellipse is a curve formed by the set of all points P such that*

$$(2) \qquad PF_1 + PF_2 = k,$$

where PF_1 *is the distance of* P *from the fixed point* F_1 *and* PF_2 *is the distance of* P *from the fixed point* F_2. *The points* F_1 *and* F_2 *are called the foci of the ellipse.*

To define a hyperbola we use the difference of the distances rather than the sum in equation (2). But since there is no preference in the order of subtraction, equation (2) is replaced by two equations as follows.

Definition 5. *A hyperbola is a curve formed by the set of all points P such that either*

(3) $$PF_1 - PF_2 = k,$$

or

(4) $$PF_2 - PF_1 = k,$$

where PF_1 and PF_2 have the same meaning as in Definition 4. The fixed points F_1 and F_2 are called the foci of the hyperbola.

A typical hyperbola is shown in Figure 7.11. Notice that it falls into two pieces. If k is positive, the right branch consists of the points that satisfy equation (3). The left branch is composed of the points that satisfy equation (4).

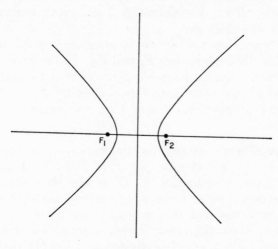

Fig. 7.11

When a rectangular coordinate system is introduced, it is a simple matter to obtain equations for these curves, and from these equations we can derive many interesting properties of the curves. But this material can be found in any book on analytic geometry, and so we omit it. Our objective is to prove that these curves are the ones obtained as sections of a cone. We will do this in § 4, 5, and 6.

Exercise 1

1. Prove that for a circle, every diameter is an axis of symmetry.

2. Prove that a square has four distinct axes of symmetry.

3. How many axes of symmetry does a rectangle have, if it is not a square?

4. How many axes of symmetry does an equilateral triangle have? How many are there for a regular pentagon?

5. How many axes of symmetry does a Star of David have? (See problem 1 exercise 3 of Chapter 5.)

6. Prove that a parabola is symmetric with respect to its axis. *Hint:* Use definition 2 and prove that certain triangles are congruent.

7. Prove that an ellipse is symmetric with respect to the line through its foci F_1 and F_2. Use definition 4.

★8. Prove that an ellipse is symmetric with respect to the perpendicular bisector of the segment F_1F_2.

★9. Repeat problems 7 and 8 for the hyperbola. Use definition 5.

4. **The ellipse.** We now have at hand two definitions of an ellipse, the first given as a part of definition 1, and the second given as definition 4. Of course there should be only one definition and any other assertion about the curve should be a theorem that is proved on the basis of the definition. With this point of view in mind, we now settle on definitions 2, 4, and 5 as our definitions of the parabola, ellipse, and hyperbola respectively and we will prove that these are the curves obtained when a plane cuts a right circular cone. We begin the program with

Theorem 3. *If a right circular cone is cut by a plane $\mathcal{P}$ in a closed curve $\mathcal{E}$ then the curve $\mathcal{E}$ is an ellipse.*

Proof. Let $\mathcal{E}$ be the curve of intersection of the plane $\mathcal{P}$ with a right circular cone, as shown in Figure 7.12. We place two spheres, S_1 and S_2, in the cone so that they are both tangent to the cone, with one above the plane $\mathcal{P}$ and one below the plane $\mathcal{P}$. The radii of these two spheres are selected so that the spheres are also tangent to the plane P (see Figure 7.12). We denote the points of tangency of the spheres S_1 and S_2 with the plane P, by F_1 and F_2 respectively. Finally, in accordance with theorem 1, we let C_1 and C_2 denote the two circles along which the two spheres are tangent to the cone.

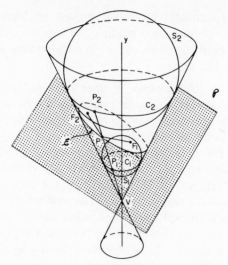

Fig. 7.12

Let us now select any point P on $\mathcal{E}$ and draw the line VP. Since the points V and P lie on the surface of the cone, so also does the entire line and hence this line meets the circles C_1 and C_2 at points that we denote by P_1 and P_2 respectively. It is clear that the length of the line segment P_1P_2 is the same for every point P on $\mathcal{E}$. But by theorem 2 $PF_1 = PP_1$ and $PF_2 = PP_2$ and hence

$$PF_1 + PF_2 = PP_1 + PP_2 = P_1P_2 = \text{a constant}$$

for every choice of P on $\mathcal{E}$. Hence $\mathcal{E}$ is an ellipse with foci at F_1 and F_2.   Q.E.D.

Exercise 2

★**1.** By definition a right circular cylinder is the surface generated by a line that moves so that it always passes through a given fixed circle, and is always perpendicular to the plane of the circle. Each line in the surface is called an *element* of the surface.

Prove that if a right circular cylinder is cut by a plane that is not parallel to an *element* of the cylinder, then the curve of intersection is an ellipse.

5. The hyperbola. It is convenient to have the axis of the right circular cone vertical. Then we can speak of the two parts of the cone, one above the vertex V, and the other below the vertex V.

Theorem 4. *If a plane P, that does not pass through the vertex of a right circular cone, meets both parts of the cone, then the curve of intersection is a hyperbola.*

Proof. Let $\mathcal{K}$ denote the curve of intersection of the plane and the cone. Just as in the proof of theorem 3, we introduce two spheres S_1 and S_2, of radii r_1 and r_2, which are tangent to the right circular cone along the circles C_1 and C_2 respectively. The sphere S_2 lies above the vertex and the sphere S_1 lies below the vertex, and the radii are so chosen that these spheres are tangent to the plane P. We denote these tangency points by F_1 and F_2 (see Figure 7.13).

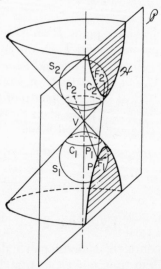

Fig. 7.13

Let P be any point on the lower branch of $\mathfrak{IC}$, the curve of intersection, and let the line VP, which lies in the surface of the cone, meet the circles C_1 and C_2 in the points P_1 and P_2 respectively. It is obvious that the length of the segment P_1P_2 is the same for every choice of the point P. But by Theorem 2 we have $PF_1 = PP_1$ and $PF_2 = PP_2$.

Since P is on the lower branch of $\mathfrak{IC}$, we have

$$PF_2 - PF_1 = PP_2 - PP_1 = P_1P_2 = \text{a constant,}$$

for every such choice of the point P. If P is selected on the upper branch we have $PP_1 - PP_2 = P_1P_2$ and in this case we find that

$$PF_1 - PF_2 = PP_1 - PP_2 = P_1P_2 = \text{a constant.}$$

Whence $\mathfrak{IC}$ is a hyperbola with foci at F_1 and F_2. Q.E.D.

6. The parabola. Finally, we must consider the case in which the plane $\mathcal{P}$ only meets one part of the cone, but the curve of intersection does not close. This happens if and only if the plane is parallel to just one of the lines in the surface of the cone.

Theorem 5. *If a plane $\mathcal{P}$ is parallel to exactly one of the elements of a right circular cone, then it intersects that cone in a parabola.*

Proof. Let $\mathcal{P}_1$ be the plane and suppose that l is the line in the surface of the cone that is parallel to $\mathcal{P}_1$. We place a sphere of radius r in the cone so that it is simultaneously tangent to the cone and the plane $\mathcal{P}_1$. Let C be the circle along which the sphere is tangent to the cone, and let F be the point at which the sphere is tangent to the plane $\mathcal{P}_1$ (see Figure 7.14).

We pass a second plane $\mathcal{P}_2$ through the circle C and let d be the line of intersection of $\mathcal{P}_1$ and $\mathcal{P}_2$. It will be seen from the proof that F is the focus of the parabola and d is the directrix.

We select any point P on the curve of intersection of the plane $\mathcal{P}_1$ and the cone, and we draw the line VP which will intersect the circle C in some point P_1. Then by theorem 2 we have $PF = PP_1$. All that remains is to prove

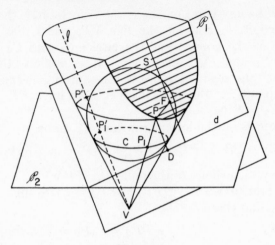

Fig. 7.14

that $PP_1 = PD$ where D is the foot of the perpendicular dropped from P to the line d. Let the plane through P, perpendicular to the axis of the cone meet l at P', and let the plane $\mathcal{P}_2$ through P_1, perpendicular to the same axis, meet the line l at P_1'. Then clearly $PP_1 = P'P_1'$. Finally the line PD is obviously parallel to l and hence $P'P_1' = PD$. Since $PF = PP_1$, $PP_1 = P'P_1'$ and $P'P_1' = PD$, we have $PF = PD$ for any choice of the point P on the curve of intersection. Consequently that curve is a parabola with focus at F and directrix d.   Q.E.D.

Exercise 3

1. If the plane $\mathcal{P}$, not containing the vertex of a right circular cone, is perpendicular to the axis, the intersection curve is a circle. Prove this statement. Since this circle is also an ellipse, where are the foci?

2. Prove theorem 2.

3. Given three lines l, p, and y construct a circle with center on y and tangent to the lines l and p (see Figure 7.15). In the proofs of theorems 3, 4, and 5 it was assumed

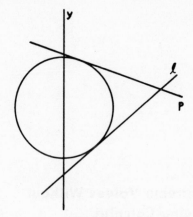

Fig. 7.15

as intuitively obvious that a sphere could be found that was simultaneously tangent to the cone and a given plane. Notice that this problem provides a rigorous proof of that fact.

4. Prove that the line segment P_1P_2 of Figure 7.12 has the same length for every point P on the intersection of the plane $\mathcal{P}$ and the cone.

5. Do the same for the segment P_1P_2 of Figure 7.13.

6. In the figure for the proof of theorem 4, the point P was selected on the lower branch of the hyperbola. Complete the proof by considering the case in which P is taken on the upper branch of the curve.

7. Complete the proof of theorem 5 by proving that (a) $PP_1 = P'P_1'$, (b) PD is parallel to $P'P_1'$, and (c) $PD = P'P_1'$, where the letters refer to Figure 7.14.

CHAPTER 8

Extreme Values Without Using Calculus

1. A taste of analytic geometry. In order to understand calculus, it is first necessary to have some familiarity with analytic geometry. Fortunately we only need to use a very small amount of analytic geometry, and this material is always covered in the freshman mathematics course of any respectable high school. In this section we give a brief survey of the material that we will need. The reader who wishes to go further may consult any of the standard books on analytic geometry.[1]

Analytic geometry is a union of algebra and geometry. The fusing agent is the rectangular coordinate system. The rectangular coordinate system in the plane provides each point in the plane with a pair of numbers, and provides each pair of numbers with a corresponding point in the plane. Here are the details on how this is done.

In the plane we erect two lines, one horizontal, and one vertical, meeting at right angles at a point O called the *origin* (see Figure 8.1). The horizontal line is called the *x-axis,* and the vertical line is called the *y-axis.* Let P be any point that lies above the x-axis and to the right of the y-axis (see Figure 8.1). From P we draw the line segments:

[1]See for example Love, *Elements of Analytic Geometry* (New York: The Macmillan Co., 1950), or Smith, Salkover, and Justice, *Analytic Geometry* (New York: John Wiley and Sons, 1954).

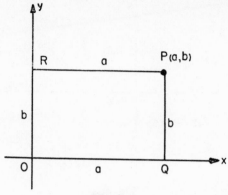

Fig. 8.1

PQ perpendicular to the x-axis, and PR perpendicular to the y-axis. Let $a = RP$ be the distance of P from the y-axis, and let $b = QP$ be the distance of P from the x-axis. Then we attach to the point P the pair of numbers (a, b). These numbers are known as the coordinates of P. The number a is called the *x-coordinate* or the *abscissa* of P and b is called the *y-coordinate* or the *ordinate* of P. Since the figure $PROQ$ is a rectangle, and the pairs of opposite sides are equal, we can say that the x-coordinate of P is the distance OQ, and that the y-coordinate of P is the distance OR. If P lies to the left of the y-axis, we again measure the distances, but this time the x-coordinate is the negative of the distance of P from the y-axis. If P lies below the x-axis then the y-coordinate is the negative of the distance of P from the x-axis. Of course if P is on some axis, then its distance from that axis is zero.

The coordinate axes divide the plane into four regions which are called *quadrants* and are customarily labeled I, II, III, and IV as indicated in Figure 8.2. That figure also shows a number of points together with their coordinates. The symbol II $(-, +)$ indicates that in quadrant II the x-coordinate is negative, and the y-coordinate is positive.

We have seen that each point P in the plane has a unique pair of numbers (x, y) attached to it. Conversely, if we are given any pair of numbers (x, y) we can locate a unique

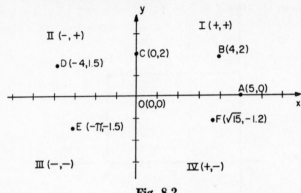

Fig. 8.2

point having those numbers as coordinates. We merely measure from O along the x-axis, the appropriate distance[2] $|x|$, proceeding to the right if x is positive and to the left if x is negative. We then turn and proceed parallel to the y-axis a distance $|y|$, upward if y is positive, and downward if y is negative. This leads to a point P with coordinates (x, y). The preceding discussion proves

Theorem 1. *With a given pair of mutually perpendicular axes, each point P in the plane has a uniquely determined pair of coordinates (x, y). Conversely each pair of coordinates (x, y) determines a unique point P in the plane with these coordinates.*

The axes together with the method of attaching coordinates to the points give the rectangular coordinate system. It is also called the Cartesian coordinate system in honor of René Descartes (1596–1650). For an interesting account of the life of Descartes see E. T. Bell, *Men of Mathematics* (New York: Simon & Schuster, 1937).

Now we can find a graph or curve for any given equation. Suppose for example that the equation is $4y = x^2$. Some points in the plane have coordinates (x, y) that satisfy this equation, and there are other points in the plane whose coordinates do not satisfy this equation. For example the coordinates $(2, 1)$ satisfy $4y = x^2$ because $4 \times 1 = 2^2$. The coordinates $(3, 7)$ do not satisfy this

[2]The absolute value sign was introduced in §8 of Chapter 1.

equation, because $4 \times 7 \neq 3^2$. If we mark all those points whose coordinates satisfy $4y = x^2$, then we will obtain a curve, called the graph of the equation $4y = x^2$. But these remarks apply to any equation.

Definition 1. *The graph of an equation in x and y is the collection of all points (x, y) whose coordinates satisfy that equation.*

Example 1. Sketch the graph of the equation $4y = x^2$.

Solution. It is obviously impossible to mark off *all* of the points whose coordinates satisfy this equation, because there are infinitely many such points. We content ourselves with listing a few of these points and then observing that these points seem to fall on a smooth curve, the curve of Figure 8.3. To obtain such a list we merely

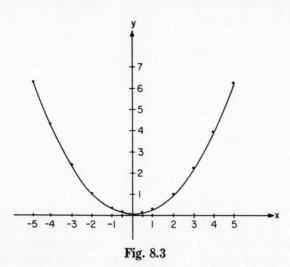

Fig. 8.3

select a few values of x and compute the associated value of y from the equation $y = \dfrac{x^2}{4}$. For example if $x = 8$, $y = \dfrac{64}{4} = 16$. Table I gives the set of x used in computing points for the graph shown in Figure 8.3. Observe that if $x = 1$, $y = \frac{1}{4}$ and if $x = -1$ we also find $y = \frac{1}{4}$. This is indicated in Table I by writing $x = \pm 1$, $y = \frac{1}{4}$.

TABLE I

x	0	$\pm\frac{1}{2}$	± 1	± 2	± 3	± 4	± 5
y	0	$\frac{1}{16}$	$\frac{1}{4}$	1	$\frac{9}{4}$	4	$\frac{25}{4}$

Example 2. Sketch the graph of the equation $y^2 = x^2$.

Solution. A little preliminary algebraic manipulation makes the task easier. For on taking square roots on both sides of $y^2 = x^2$, we find that either $y = x$ or $y = -x$.

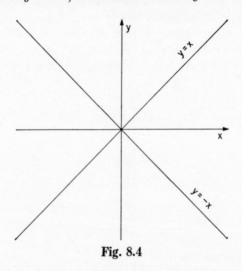

Fig. 8.4

We leave it to the reader to make a table of values. The graph of $y = x$ appears to be a straight line through the origin that makes an angle of $45°$ with the positive x-axis, and the graph of $y = -x$ appears to be a line perpendicular to this line at the origin. The graph of $y^2 = x^2$ is the pair of straight lines shown in Figure 8.4.

Exercise 1

1. On a rectangular coordinate system mark those points with the following coordinates: $(-5, -2)$, $(-3, 0)$, $(-2, 1)$, $(0, 3)$, $(4, 7)$, and $(10, 13)$. Do these points seem to lie on a straight line?

2. Draw the graph of $y = x + 3$.

In problems 3 through 6 the graph of the given equation is a straight line. Find two points whose coordinates satisfy the given equation, draw the line, and then check that other points whose coordinates satisfy the equation also seem to lie on the line.

3. $y = 3 - x$ **4.** $y = 2x - 5$

5. $y = 5 - 2x$ **6.** $3y = x + 6$

7. Sketch the graph of the equations (a) $y = x^2$ (b) $y = x^2/4$ (c) $y = x^2/10$ and (d) $y = -x^2$, all with the same set of coordinate axes.

In problems 8 through 13 sketch the graph of the given equation.

8. $y = x^3$ ★**9.** $y = |x|$

★**10.** $y = 2 - |x - 3|$ ★**11.** $y^2 = x$

★**12.** $x^2 + y^2 = 25$ ★**13.** $y = x^2 - 6x$

2. What calculus can do. Let us consider the particular function

(1) $$y = \frac{6x - x^2 + 15}{2}.$$

The graph of this equation is shown in Figure 8.5, together with the table of values used to locate some of the points on the curve.

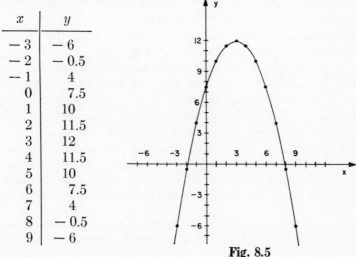

x	y
-3	-6
-2	-0.5
-1	4
0	7.5
1	10
2	11.5
3	12
4	11.5
5	10
6	7.5
7	4
8	-0.5
9	-6

Fig. 8.5

Two questions occur quite naturally with respect to this graph.

I. What is the high point on the curve of Figure 8.5? In other words for what value of x, does y, given by equation (1), attain its greatest value? What is this greatest value?

II. What is the area enclosed by the curve and the x-axis? Or what is the area of the figure which lies simultaneously below the curve and above the x-axis?

If we use calculus we can answer both of these questions. Indeed calculus, invented almost simultaneously by Newton and Leibniz,[3] gives a systematic way of answering such questions as these, not only for the particular function plotted in Figure 8.5, but for any elementary function.

Both of these questions can also be answered without using calculus, but the work involved in answering question II is intricate and lies outside the scope of this book. We will devote this chapter to question I and questions of a similar type.

3. The maximum value of a function. Precision requires that we give

Definition 2. *The number y_M is called the maximum value for the function $f(x)$, if for some x_0, the function takes on the value y_M, and if for all other values of x, the corresponding y is less than or equal to y_M.*

Restated in symbols: there is an x_0 such that $y_M = f(x_0)$, and for all other values of x, $f(x) \leqq y_M$.

For example, if we look at the graph in Figure 8.5 for the function $f(x) = (6x - x^2 + 15)/2$ it appears as though 12 is the maximum, and that this value of y occurs at $x = 3$. If 12 is the maximum, we would write $y_M = 12$ and $x_0 = 3$. The high point would then be $(3, 12)$.

Let us try to prove that 12 is the maximum value for the function (1). We begin by bringing the suspect 12 out in the open where it can be seen; namely we add and subtract 12 on the right side of (1) obtaining

---

[3] Isaac Newton, 1642–1727, and Gottfried Wilhelm Leibniz, 1646-1716. See E. T. Bell, *Men of Mathematics*, for an account of the lives of these two geniuses.

$$y = 12 + \frac{6x - x^2 + 15}{2} - 12.$$

Combining the last two terms in the usual way gives

$$y = 12 + \frac{6x - x^2 + 15 - 24}{2} = 12 + \frac{6x - x^2 - 9}{2}$$

or, on changing signs in the numerator of the fraction

$$y = 12 - \frac{x^2 - 6x + 9}{2},$$

or finally

(2) $$y = 12 - \frac{(x - 3)^2}{2}.$$

Equation (2) gives the whole story. The term $(x - 3)^2/2$ is always positive unless $x = 3$. Since it is subtracted from 12, y is always less than 12, unless $x = 3$. Therefore we have proved that:

The function $y = (6x - x^2 + 15)/2$ has a maximum at $x_0 = 3$, and the maximum value $y_M = 12$. The high point on the curve is $(3, 12)$.

Let us look at this same problem again, only this time let us suppose that we do not suspect that 12 is the maximum value of y. This is the case, if we do not make a graph of the function. Since the numerator of

(1) $$y = \frac{6x - x^2 + 15}{2}$$

is a second degree polynomial in x, we try to make it into a perfect square. The first step is to introduce a negative sign in front and change the signs throughout, obtaining

$$y = -\frac{x^2 - 6x - 15}{2}.$$

The purpose of this step is to obtain x^2 in the numerator rather than $-x^2$. We now complete the square by adding 9 to $x^2 - 6x$ and then subtracting it again in the numerator. This gives

$$y = -\frac{x^2 - 6x + 9 - 9 - 15}{2}$$

$$= -\frac{(x-3)^2 - 9 - 15}{2} = -\frac{(x-3)^2 - 24}{2}$$

or finally

$$(2) \qquad y = 12 - \frac{(x-3)^2}{2}.$$

But now just as before we deduce from (2) that 12 is the maximum value of y, and this time we did not need a graph to aid us in guessing the maximum.

4. The minimum value of a function. If we turn any curve upside down, what was a maximum, or high point on the curve, becomes a minimum or low point on the curve, and vice versa. This turning upside down can be done by rotating the curve about the x-axis. Algebraically this merely amounts to replacing y by $-y$. If this is done for the function defined by equation (1), we have $-y = (6x - x^2 + 15)/2$, or what amounts to the same thing

$$(3) \qquad y = \frac{x^2 - 6x - 15}{2}.$$

The graph of this function, together with a table of values is shown in Figure 8.6.

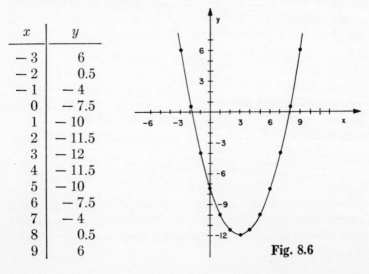

x	y
-3	6
-2	0.5
-1	-4
0	-7.5
1	-10
2	-11.5
3	-12
4	-11.5
5	-10
6	-7.5
7	-4
8	0.5
9	6

Fig. 8.6

Thus our work in § 3 convinces us that the point $(3, -12)$ is a low point or minimum point for the graph of equation (3). To be precise we give

Definition 3. *The number y_m is called the minimum value of a function $f(x)$, if for some x_0, the function takes on the value y_m, and if for all other values of x, the corresponding y is greater than or equal to y_m.*

Restated in symbols, there is an x_0 such that $y_m = f(x_0)$, and for all other values of x, $f(x) \geqq y_m$.

Thus for the function $y = (x^2 - 6x - 15)/2$, we have $x_0 = 3$, and $y_m = -12$ for the minimum. We could also prove this directly, instead of referring back to the work of § 3. Indeed, manipulating with equation (3) we find that

$$y = -12 + \frac{x^2 - 6x - 15}{2} + 12$$

$$= -12 + \frac{x^2 - 6x - 15 + 24}{2} = -12 + \frac{x^2 - 6x + 9}{2}$$

$$= -12 + \frac{(x-3)^2}{2}.$$

Therefore $y = -12$ plus something which is positive except when $x = 3$. Whence $y \geqq -12$ and $y = -12$ only when $x = 3$. Q.E.D.

Exercise 2

In problems 1 through 6 make a graph of the function and then guess at the maximum (or minimum) value of the function. Prove that your guess for the maximum (or minimum) value is correct.

1. $y = x^2 - 4x + 7$. **2.** $y = 12x - x^2 - 26$.
3. $y = -x^2 - 8x - 21$. **4.** $y = x^2 + 2x - 13$.
5. $y = \dfrac{19 + 2x - x^2}{4}$. **6.** $y = \dfrac{x^2 + 4x - 8}{6}$.

In problems 7 through 12 make a graph of the function and use the graph to find the coordinates of the high point or the low point on the curve, if the curve has one. Do not attempt a proof.

7. $y = 3x - 5$.   8. $y = x^3$.
9. $y = 3 + | x - 2 |$.   10. $y = 2 - | x - 5 |$.
11. $y = \dfrac{8}{1 + x^2}$.   12. $y = \dfrac{3 + x}{1 - x}$.

★5. The relative maximum and relative minimum. The alert reader has already noticed that the two preceding examples, and the first six problems of exercise 2, all involve quadratic functions of x. What happens if the polynomial in x is a cubic, or of a higher degree? As an example let us consider the function

(4) $$y = x^3 - 3x^2 - 9x + 13.$$

The graph of this function is shown in Figure 8.7, together

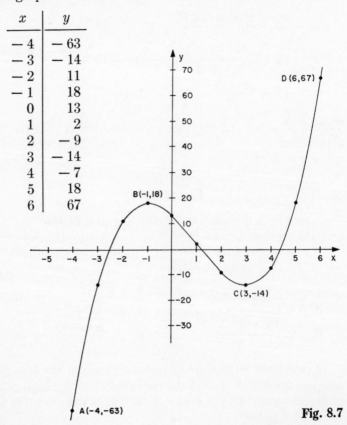

x	y
-4	-63
-3	-14
-2	11
-1	18
0	13
1	2
2	-9
3	-14
4	-7
5	18
6	67

Fig. 8.7

with a table of values used to locate some of the points on the curve. Observe that for convenience we have selected different size units on the two axes.

At first glance the bumps at B $(-1, 18)$ and C $(3, -14)$ give the appearance of being high and low points on the curve. But at $x = 6$, $y = 67$ so B is certainly not a maximum point. Similarly C cannot be a minimum point since at $x = -4$, $y = -63$. Still the points B and C are interesting and deserve some special name. As we will prove shortly, if x is *near* to -1, then $y \leqq 18$. For this reason B is called a *relative maximum point*. Similarly C is called a *relative minimum point*.

Definition 4. *Let $y = f(x)$ and let $y_M = f(x_0)$. Suppose there is a neighborhood of x_0*

(4) $$x_0 - d < x < x_0 + d$$

such that for all x in the neighborhood, i.e. for all x satisfying (4), we have

(5) $$f(x) \leqq y_M,$$

then y_M is called a relative maximum for the function and the point (x_0, y_M) is called a relative maximum point.

If $y_m = f(x_0)$ and if for all x in a neighborhood of x_0,

(6) $$f(x) \geqq y_m$$

then y_m is called a relative minimum for the function, and the point (x_0, y_m) is called a relative minimum point.

The graph in Figure 8.7 suggests that B $(-1, 18)$ is a relative maximum point and that C $(3, -14)$ is a relative minimum point for the function $y = x^3 - 3x^2 - 9x + 13$. We will prove that this is so. Just as in the case of the quadratic function (1), we put the relative maximum 18, out in front where it can be seen, by adding and subtracting the same quantity on the right side of (4). Thus

$$\begin{aligned}
y &= 18 + x^3 - 3x^2 - 9x + 13 - 18 \\
&= 18 + x^3 - 3x^2 - 9x - 5 \\
&= 18 + (x + 1)(x^2 - 4x - 5) \\
&= 18 + (x + 1)(x + 1)(x - 5) \\
&= 18 - (x + 1)^2(5 - x).
\end{aligned}$$

The factor $(x + 1)^2$ is always greater than or equal to zero and the factor $5 - x$ is positive for $x < 5$ and is certainly positive for x near -1. Therefore if x is near to -1, the quantity $(x + 1)^2(5 - x)$ is positive or zero, so something is subtracted from 18. The subtracted term is zero at $x = -1$. Therefore 18 is a relative maximum for this function.

Similarly for the point $(3, -14)$ we proceed thus:

$$\begin{aligned} y &= -14 + x^3 - 3x^2 - 9x + 13 + 14 \\ &= -14 + x^3 - 3x^2 - 9x + 27 \\ &= -14 + (x - 3)(x^2 - 9) \\ &= -14 + (x - 3)^2(x + 3). \end{aligned}$$

Therefore for x near 3 something is added to -14, and this added term is positive or zero, and is zero only for $x = 3$. Consequently the point $(3, -14)$ is a relative minimum.

Exercise 3

For each of the following functions, make a graph and then guess at the relative maximum and minimum points on the graph. Then prove that your guess is correct.

★1. $y = 1 + 3x^2 - x^3$.
★2. $y = x^3 - 9x^2 + 15x + 4$.
★3. $y = 7 + 36x + 3x^2 - 2x^3$.
★4. $y = x^3 + 3x^2 - 24x - 11$.
★★5. $y = 1 + 8x^2 - x^4$.
★★★6. $y = x^4 - 4x^3 - 2x^2 + 12x + 13$.

6. Some simple applications. Here are a number of natural problems which can be solved by the methods just developed.

Example 1. Find two numbers whose sum is 12 and whose product is as large as possible.

Solution. We have an intuitive feeling that these numbers should be 6 and 6. Let x and y be the two numbers. Then $x + y = 12$ and we are to find the maximum of the product xy. This product involves two variables, but we can eliminate one of them by using the fact that

$y = 12 - x$. Hence we must maximize the product

$$(6) \qquad P = xy = x(12 - x) = 12x - x^2.$$

Since we suspect that the maximum occurs when $x = 6$, and that $P_M = 6 \times 6 = 36$, we add and subtract 36 on the right side of (6). We find that

$$P = 36 + 12x - x^2 - 36$$
$$= 36 - (x^2 - 12x + 36)$$
$$= 36 - (x - 6)^2.$$

Since $(x - 6)^2 \geqq 0$ for all x it is obvious that $P \leqq 36$, with equality if and only if $x = 6$. \hfill Q.E.D.

Example 2. An enclosure in the form of a rectangle is to be made using 2400 feet of wire fence. What should be the dimensions of the rectangular enclosure in order that the enclosed area be a maximum?

Solution. This is just a disguised form of Example 1. For if x and y denote the lengths of the sides of the rectangle then we must have

$$(7) \qquad 2x + 2y = 2400$$

in order to use all of the fencing available. The area in square feet is the product

$$(8) \qquad P = xy$$

and this is the expression we must maximize. Equation (7) gives $y = 1200 - x$ and using this in (8) yields

$$(9) \qquad P = x(1200 - x).$$

This quantity differs from (6) only in the extra zeros following the 12, so we may guess that the maximum occurs when $x = 600$. Proceeding in the usual way

$$P = 600^2 + 1200x - x^2 - 600^2$$
$$= 600^2 - (x - 600)^2 \leqq 600^2.$$

Whence the maximum area enclosed is 360,000 square feet, and the enclosure for this area is a square 600 feet on each side.

It is intuitively obvious from these two examples, that

among all the rectangles with a given fixed perimeter, the one with the largest area is a square (see problem 4 of exercise 4).

Example 3. Suppose that the land of example 2 is bounded on one side by a river with a straight bank so that the rectangular enclosure is open on one side (see Figure 8.8). What should be the dimensions of this open rectangle in order that the area be a maximum?

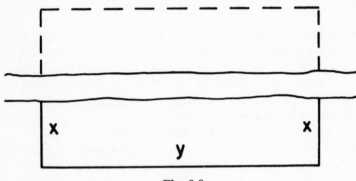

Fig. 8.8

Long solution. Let x and y denote the lengths of the sides as indicated in the figure. Then we must have

$$(10) \qquad 2x + y = 2400$$

in order to use all the fencing. Again the product $P = xy$ gives the area, but now from equation (10) we have $y = 2400 - 2x$. Substituting for y gives

$$P = x(2400 - 2x) = 2400x - 2x^2$$
$$= 2(1200x - x^2) = -2(x^2 - 1200x).$$

It is not clear what we should conjecture for the maximum value of P, but we can complete the square in the parentheses by adding 600^2 inside, and making the proper adjustment outside. When this is done we find that

$$P = -2(x^2 - 1200x + 600^2) + 2 \times 600^2$$
$$= 720,000 - 2(x - 600)^2.$$

Whence it is obvious that $P \leqq 720{,}000$ and that the equality sign occurs when $x = 600$. Then from (10) we find that $y = 1200$.

The presence of a river on one side allows us to double the area enclosed with the same amount of wire.

Short solution. Let P be the area of the open rectangle formed from the given wire. We imagine that our supply of wire is doubled so that we can construct a second open rectangle that is the reflection of the first one in the river's edge. This second rectangle is shown dotted in Figure 8.8. Then the area enclosed by both rectangles is $2P$. But $2P$ is a maximum when the enclosure is a square (see problem 4 of exercise 4). Therefore P is a maximum when $y = 2x$. Using this in (10) gives $x = 600$ and hence $y = 1200$.

Q.E.D.

Some problems can be solved without algebraic manipulations. This is illustrated in

Example 4. A triangle is inscribed in a fixed semicircle of radius r so that the base of the triangle coincides with the diameter (Figure 8.9). What is the maximum for the area of the triangle?

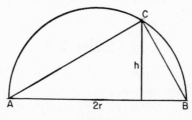

Fig. 8.9

Solution. Since the area of this inscribed triangle is given by

$$A = \tfrac{1}{2}bh = \tfrac{1}{2}(2r)h = rh$$

and r is fixed, the area is a maximum when h is a maximum. Obviously h is a maximum when the vertex point C bisects the arc AB, and in this case $h = r$. Therefore $A \leqq r^2$ with equality if and only if $\angle BAC = 45°$.

Example 5. Find the maximum of the function $f(x) = x\sqrt{a^2 - x^2}$ where a is some positive constant.

Solution. Observe that the radical is not real if $x > a$. Further if $x < 0$, then $f(x)$ is negative. Hence in solving this problem we can restrict our attention to x in the interval $0 \leqq x \leqq a$. But then the solution of this problem follows *immediately* from example 4. To see this let $BC = x$ (in Figure 8.9) and let $2r = a$. Since the triangle ACB is a right triangle ($\angle ACB$ is inscribed in a semi-circle), $AC = \sqrt{4r^2 - x^2} = \sqrt{a^2 - x^2}$. Whence the area of the triangle is given by

$$\text{Area} = \tfrac{1}{2}BC \cdot AC = \tfrac{1}{2}x\sqrt{a^2 - x^2} = \tfrac{1}{2}f(x).$$

But from example 4, we know that the maximum for the area is r^2 and this maximum is achieved when $BC = \sqrt{2}r$. It follows that the maximum value of $f(x)$ is $2r^2$ and is achieved also when $x = \sqrt{2}r$. Recalling that $r = a/2$, we conclude that

$$x\sqrt{a^2 - x^2} \leqq \frac{a^2}{2}$$

and the equality sign occurs if and only if $x = a/\sqrt{2}$.

Exercise 4

1. Find two numbers whose sum is 20 and whose product is as large as possible.

2. Find two numbers whose sum is 38 and whose product is as large as possible.

★3. Find two numbers whose sum is a given positive constant s, and whose product is as large as possible.

4. Prove that among all rectangles with the same perimeter $4L$, the one with the largest area is the square with side L.

5. A rectangle is inscribed in a fixed circle of radius r. Find the maximum value of its area. *Hint:* Draw a diagonal and use the result of example 4.

★6. Find the area of the largest rectangle that can be inscribed in an acute-angled triangle with base 10 and height 6. *Hint:* In Figure 8.10 let $x = RS$ and $y = CP$. Then using similar triangles show that $x = 5y/3$ and that area $= 5y(6 - y)/3$.

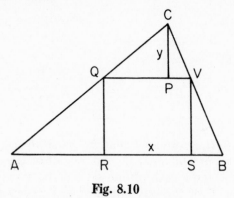

Fig. 8.10

★★7. Generalize the preceding problem by inscribing the rectangle in an acute-angled triangle with base b and height h. *Hint:* As before prove that $x = by/h$ and that area $= by(h - y)/h$, and find the maximum area.

★7. **More complicated examples.** We have proved in Chapter 4 that the geometric mean is always less than or equal to the arithmetic mean for any set of positive numbers. If we have just 3 numbers, this states that

$$(9) \qquad \sqrt[3]{a_1 a_2 a_3} \leqq \frac{a_1 + a_2 + a_3}{3},$$

or equivalently, by cubing both sides of (9),

$$(10) \qquad a_1 a_2 a_3 \leqq \frac{(a_1 + a_2 + a_3)^3}{27}.$$

Furthermore the equality sign occurs if and only if all of the numbers are the same. This inequality is useful in

Example 1. A box with an open top is to be made from an 18 by 18 inch square sheet of metal by cutting out the corners (see Figure 8.11) and turning up the edges. What size cut should be made to obtain a box with maximum volume?

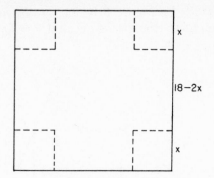

Fig. 8.11

Solution. It is obvious that in order to obtain a box the 4 pieces cut out must be squares all of the same size. Let x denote the length of one side of the square cut out. The volume V of the box obtained is $V = lwh$ and hence

$$(11) \qquad V = (18 - 2x)(18 - 2x)x.$$

This is a product of three factors similar to the left side of (10), but unfortunately the sum of these factors is *not a constant*. Indeed for the sum we have $s = 18 - 2x + 18 - 2x + x = 36 - 3x$. But this is easily fixed. We multiply both sides of (11) by 4 and obtain

$$(12) \qquad 4V = (18 - 2x)(18 - 2x)4x$$

where now for the sum of the factors, $s = 18 - 2x + 18 - 2x + 4x = 36$, a constant. Then applying the inequality (10) to (12) we find that

$$4V \leqq \frac{s^3}{27} = \frac{(36)^3}{27} = (12)^3,$$

and consequently $V \leqq 432$ cubic inches. Further the equality sign occurs when the factors are the same. This gives $18 - 2x = 4x$, and hence $x = 3$. Thus the largest box that can be made from this piece of metal has dimensions 12 by 12 by 3 inches.

Example 2. Find the minimum value of the function

$$(13) \qquad y = ax^2 + bx + c$$

where a, b, and c are constants and $a > 0$.

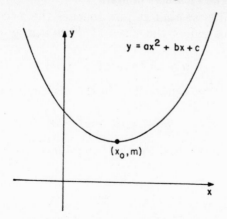

$y = ax^2 + bx + c$

(x_0, m)

Fig. 8.12

Solution. The graph of this function is a parabola as indicated in Figure 8.12. If x is very large the term ax^2 is dominant, and since $a > 0$, the parabola turns upward as indicated in Figure 8.12.

If the curve intersects the x-axis, the points of intersection can be found by setting $y = 0$. Then (13) becomes

$$0 = ax^2 + bx + c$$

and by the quadratic formula the solutions are

$$(14) \qquad x_1, x_2 = \frac{-b \pm \sqrt{b^2 - 4ac}}{2a}.$$

The curve need not touch the x-axis at all. If this is the case then the solutions given by (14) cannot be real. Consequently if the curve does not touch the x-axis then $b^2 - 4ac$ is negative. If the curve intersects the x-axis in two points, then $b^2 - 4ac$ must be positive, in order to give two real solutions in (14). The intermediate stage in which the curve is tangent to the x-axis occurs when $b^2 - 4ac = 0$, because in this case (14) gives just one value of x for which $y = 0$. Because of its great significance the quantity $b^2 - 4ac$ is called the *discriminant* of the quadratic expression $ax^2 + bx + c$.

We use the above remarks to find the minimum of $ax^2 + bx + c$. Let m denote this minimum. If we subtract m from the right side of (13) this merely lowers the curve m units, so that it just touches the x-axis (if m is negative this raises the curve). Then the graph of the function

$$y = ax^2 + bx + (c - m)$$

just touches the x-axis. Hence the discriminant must be zero, *i.e.*

$$b^2 - 4a(c - m) = 0.$$

Solving for m, we find for the minimum

$$(15) \qquad m = \frac{4ac - b^2}{4a}.$$

★★Example 3. If $a_1, a_2, \cdots, a_n$ and $b_1, b_2, \cdots, b_n$ are any two sets of numbers, prove that

$$(16) \quad (a_1b_1 + a_2b_2 + \cdots + a_nb_n)^2$$
$$\leqq (a_1^2 + a_2^2 + \cdots + a_n^2)(b_1^2 + b_2^2 + \cdots + b_n^2).$$

This is known as the Cauchy inequality.[4]

Solution. For any x we have

$$(17) \qquad \begin{aligned} (a_1x + b_1)^2 &= a_1^2x^2 + 2a_1b_1x + b_1^2 \geqq 0, \\ (a_2x + b_2)^2 &= a_2^2x^2 + 2a_2b_2x + b_2^2 \geqq 0, \\ &\vdots \\ (a_nx + b_n)^2 &= a_n^2x^2 + 2a_nb_nx + b_n^2 \geqq 0. \end{aligned}$$

Let us add all of these inequalities. The result is an inequality of second degree in x, namely

$$(a_1^2 + a_2^2 + \cdots + a_n^2)x^2 + (2a_1b_1 + 2a_2b_2 + \cdots + 2a_nb_n)x$$
$$+ b_1^2 + b_2^2 + \cdots + b_n^2 \geqq 0.$$

If we let A, B, and C denote the coefficients of the polynomial in x, we can write this briefly as

$$(18) \qquad Ax^2 + Bx + C \geqq 0,$$

[4]Augustin Louis Cauchy (1789–1857) was the most prolific of the French mathematicians. His collected works fill twenty-six volumes, all on mathematics and most of it original contributions.

where

$$(19) \qquad A = a_1^2 + a_2^2 + \cdots + a_n^2,$$
$$(20) \qquad B = 2(a_1 b_1 + a_2 b_2 + \cdots + a_n b_n),$$

and

$$(21) \qquad C = b_1^2 + b_2^2 + \cdots + b_n^2.$$

Since the inequality (18) is valid for all real x, the graph of $y = Ax^2 + Bx + C$ does not cut the real axis, and at worst merely touches it. Therefore the discriminant of of (18) must be negative or zero, *i.e.*

$$(22) \qquad\qquad B^2 - 4AC \leqq 0.$$

Using (19), (20) and (21) in (22) gives (16).   Q.E.D.

Exercise 5

1. Find the dimensions of the largest box (open on top) that can be made from a sheet of metal 24 by 24 inches.

2. Repeat problem 1 using a square piece of metal of side L.

★3. If $a < 0$, prove that the maximum M of the function $y = ax^2 + bx + c$ is given by

$$M = \frac{4ac - b^2}{4a}.$$

Compare this expression with (15).

★4. Use the methods of § 4 to solve example 2 of § 7.

5. Use the general formulas just developed to find the extreme values (maximum or minimum) for the functions in problems 1 through 6 of exercise 2.

6. Verify the identity
$$(a_1^2 + a_2^2)(b_1^2 + b_2^2) - (a_1 b_1 + a_2 b_2)^2 = (a_1 b_2 - a_2 b_1)^2$$
and use this identity to give an alternate proof of Cauchy's inequality in the simple case $n = 2$.

7. Use Cauchy's inequality to prove that
$$(a_1 + a_2 + \cdots + a_n)^2 \leqq n(a_1^2 + a_2^2 + \cdots + a_n^2).$$

★8. Prove that if all of the variables are positive, then
$$(a_1 b_1 + a_2 b_2 + \cdots + a_n b_n)^2 \geqq n^2 (a_1 a_2 \cdots a_n b_1 b_2 \cdots b_n)^{2/n}.$$
The Cauchy inequality gives an upper bound for the left side of (16). This problem provides a lower bound.

CHAPTER 9

Geometric Extremes

1. Two simple examples. The simple and obvious remark that "a straight line is the shortest path between two points" permits us to solve quite easily a number of problems that would otherwise be troublesome. Before giving some examples we must first review a topic that was mentioned briefly in Chapter 7 (see Exercise 1 of Chapter 7).

Two points P_1 and P_2 are said to be *symmetric with respect to a line l* if the line l is the perpendicular bisector of the segment P_1P_2. Each of the points is said to be the *reflection* of the other point in the line l. Either point is also said to be the *mirror image* of the other point in the line l. Given a point P_1 and a line l, the mirror image of P_1 in l is uniquely determined and in fact can be constructed using the compass and straightedge as indicated in Figure 9.1. Conversely given P_1 and P_2, there is just

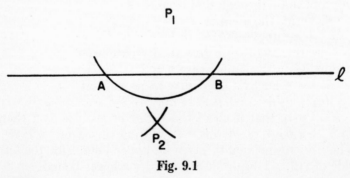

Fig. 9.1

one line in which each of these points is the reflection of the other, and this line is easy to construct since it is just the perpendicular bisector of the segment P_1P_2.

What do we mean by the image of some figure F_1 in a line l? It is just the figure F_2 consisting of all those points which are the mirror image of some point of F_1 in l. For example, referring to Figure 9.2, the mirror image of the

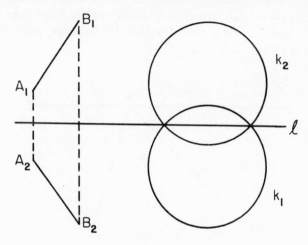

Fig. 9.2

line segment A_1B_1 in l is just the line segment A_2B_2 and the reflection of the circle k_1 in that same line is the circle k_2.

A figure is said to be symmetric in a line l if the figure is its own reflection in the line. Stated differently the figure F is symmetric in a line l if whenever P is a point of F, then the mirror image of P in l is also a point of F. The line l is called an *axis of symmetry for the figure*.

As examples we cite the following:

(a) A circle is symmetric with respect to any diameter.

(b) A pair of intersecting circles with equal radii forms a figure that is symmetric with respect to their common chord (*i.e.* the line joining the points of intersection).

(c) A pair of circles (intersecting or not, equal radii or

not) is symmetric with respect to the line joining their centers.

(*d*) A rectangle is symmetric with respect to a diagonal if and only if the rectangle is a square.

(*e*) The reflection of a triangle in a given line, is a second triangle congruent to the first (see problems 6 and 8 of exercise 1).

With these concepts firmly in mind we are ready for

Example 1. Given points *P* and *Q* on the same side of a line *l*, find the shortest path from *P* to some point on *l* and then back to *Q* (Figure 9.3).

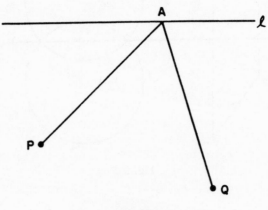

Fig. 9.3

This example has some interesting interpretations. The path *PAQ* can be regarded as the path of a boat between two fixed points, with a landing at some place on the shore. It can also be regarded as the path of a ray of light from *P* to *Q*, reflected at the point *A* by a mirror *l*. In either case we are searching for the location of the point *A* which will make the length of the path traveled by the boat or light ray a minimum.

Solution. Let *A* be any fixed point on the line *l*, and construct the segment *AQ'* which is the image of the segment *AQ* in *l* (see Figure 9.4). Since *QR = Q'R* it is obvi-

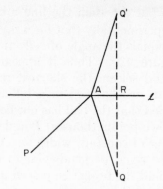

Fig. 9.4

ous that $\triangle ARQ \cong \triangle ARQ'$ so that $AQ = AQ'$ and hence the polygonal path PAQ' has the same length as the path PAQ.

Since a straight line is the shortest path between two points it is at once obvious that of all paths joining the fixed points P and Q', the shortest one is the straight line. But, as indicated in Figure 9.5, this locates the point A as the intersection point of the line l and the segment PQ'. If $A\star$ denotes this intersection point, then the path $PA\star Q$ is the shortest of all paths from P to the line l and thence to Q.

We leave it for the student to prove that if n is a line

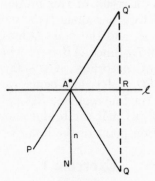

Fig. 9.5

perpendicular to l at $A^\star$ then the line n bisects $\angle PA^\star Q$.

It is known experimentally that for a ray of light the angle of incidence equals the angle of reflection ($\angle PA^\star N = \angle NA^\star Q$ in Figure 9.5). Thus it appears that light is naturally lazy and selects the shortest path. The same lazy behavior can be observed in a billiard ball striking a cushion, provided that the ball has not been given a spin.

Example 2. Two points (houses) P and Q are separated by a straight river of constant width w. A bridge is to be erected across the river, perpendicular to the direction of flow. Where should the bridge be placed in order that the path between P and Q has minimum length (Figure 9.6)?

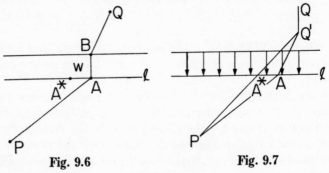

Fig. 9.6   Fig. 9.7

Solution. As indicated in Figure 9.6 we are to minimize the sum $PA + AB + BQ$. In order to locate A for a minimum path we collapse the river by moving each point above the river a distance w toward the lower bank l of the river. As a result of this motion, the two banks of the river come together along l, the point B moves into coincidence with A, and the point Q moves to Q' as indicated in Figure 9.7. Since $AB = w$, which is a constant for any location of the bridge, it is sufficient to minimize $PA + BQ$. But $BQ = AQ'$, and hence we are to minimize $PA + AQ'$. But the line segment PQ' is the shortest path between P and Q', so that the bridge should be located at $A^\star$, the intersection point of the line PQ' with l.

Exercise 1

1. Prove that the construction indicated in Figure 9.1,

gives a point P_2 which is the mirror image of P_1 in l, if in that construction $P_1A = AP_2 = BP_2$.

2. Does a line segment have an axis of symmetry?

3. Is there a figure, not a circle, that has three concurrent axes of symmetry?

4. Prove that a straight line has infinitely many axes of symmetry, all perpendicular to the line.

★**5.** Prove that if a figure has two distinct axes of symmetry that are parallel then the figure is unbounded. (A figure is said to be *unbounded* if given any circle, no matter how large, the figure has points outside of the circle.)

6. Prove that the reflection of a line segment in a line l is another line segment of the same length.

7. Prove that the reflection of a circle is a circle with the same radius.

8. Prove that the reflection of an angle is another angle congruent to the first.

9. Prove that the line n of Figure 9.5 bisects $\angle PA\star Q$.

★**10.** Prove that among all triangles with a given fixed base c and a given area A, the one with the smallest perimeter is an isosceles triangle with $a = b$.

★**11.** Given two rays l and m that meet at O and two fixed points P and Q lying between l and m, locate a point

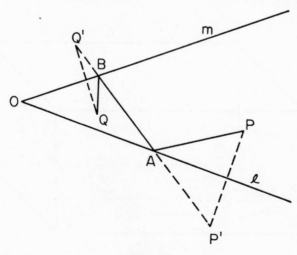

Fig. 9.8

A on l and a point B on m such that the polygonal path $PABQ$ will have minimum length. *Hint:* Give a straight-edge and compass construction for the points A and B as indicated in Figure 9.8.

★**12.** Given a fixed point C lying inside an acute angle, locate points A and B, one on each side of the angle so that the triangle ABC will have its perimeter as small as possible.

★**13.** Two points P and Q are separated by two parallel rivers of width w_1 and w_2 respectively. Bridges are to be erected over the rivers perpendicular to the direction of flow. Locate the position of these two bridges so that the path from P to Q will have a minimum length.

2. The spider and the fly. A spider 1 foot above the floor on the wall at one end of a room noticed a fly 8 feet above the floor on the opposite end of the room. Both were located exactly on the vertical bisector of the wall. The spider, anxious to become intimately acquainted with the fly, decided to walk to him along the shortest path. If the dimensions of the room are 21 feet by 10 feet by 10 feet, what path should the spider take?

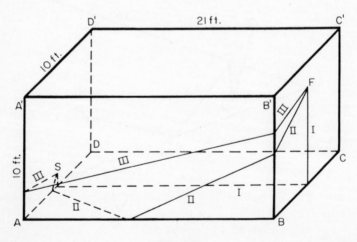

Fig. 9.9

Figure 9.9 gives a picture of the situation, together with a number of paths that the spider can follow. It is obvious that if he selects the direct route (Path I), then he must travel $(1 + 21 + 8)$ feet or a total of 30 feet. But it is conceivable that the distance travelled might be smaller on some of the other paths indicated in Figure 9.9. To investigate this possibility the spider must compute the distance for Path III. In order to assist the spider in his computation we consider the room as cut along the edges AD, DD', $D'A'$, DC, BC, CC', and $C'B'$. Then the surface of the room can be spread out on a plane, as shown in Figure 9.10.

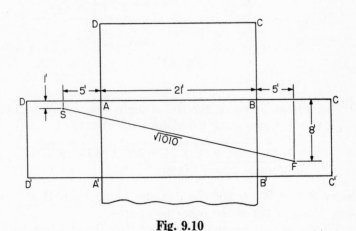

Fig. 9.10

To minimize the distance along Path III, we draw a straight line from S to F in the spread out plane of Figure 9.10. By the Pythagorean Theorem the distance travelled on Path III is

$$d = \sqrt{(8-1)^2 + (21+5+5)^2} = \sqrt{49+961} = \sqrt{1010}.$$

Since $1010 > 900 = 30^2$, the distance along Path I is less than along Path III.

It remains for the spider to investigate Path II. This time the cuts are along the edges DD', $D'A'$, $A'A$, DC,

BC, CC', and $C'B'$ and the resulting figure after the surface is spread out is shown in Figure 9.11. Using the

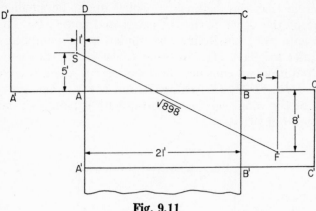

Fig. 9.11

Pythagorean Theorem for the straight line SF of Figure 9.11, the distance travelled along Path II is

$$d = \sqrt{(5+8)^2 + (1+21+5)^2} = \sqrt{13^2 + 27^2}$$
$$= \sqrt{169 + 729} = \sqrt{898}.$$

Since $898 < 900 = 30^2$ the distance along Path II *is less than* along either of the other two paths.

This does not complete the proof that the shortest path from S to F is the straight line of Figure 9.11. To complete the proof of this fact we mention that by symmetry any path around the back will be equal to the corresponding path around the front obtained by reflecting the path in a vertical plane bisecting the ends of the room. As for paths over the top, these will in general be longer, because the height of the room, 10 feet, exceeds the sum $(1+8)$ feet. We leave it to the reader to ignore, or think through in detail, this last portion of the proof.

3. More about the conic sections. We recall that an ellipse is the curve generated by a point P that moves in such a way that the sum of its distances from two fixed points F_1 and F_2 is always a constant. It is obvious that this curve separates the plane into two regions, one of which consists of points outside the ellipse, and the other consists of points inside the ellipse. A glance at Figure 9.12 is sufficient to establish

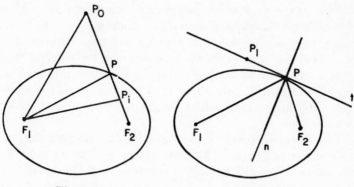

Fig. 9.12   **Fig. 9.13**

Theorem 1. *The ellipse[1] $PF_1 + PF_2 = 2a$ divides the plane into two regions. For points P_0 lying outside the ellipse*

(1) $$P_0F_1 + P_0F_2 > 2a,$$

and for points P_i lying inside the ellipse

(2) $$P_iF_1 + P_iF_2 < 2a.$$

We can use this theorem to give a simple proof of

Theorem 2. *Let P be any point on an ellipse, let t be a line tangent to the ellipse at P and let n be a line perpendicular to t at P (see Figure 9.13). Then the line n bisects $\angle F_1PF_2$, where F_1 and F_2 are the foci of the ellipse.*

Proof. Since P is on the ellipse we have $PF_1 + PF_2 = 2a$. Suppose that the line n does not bisect $\angle F_1PF_2$. Then by example 1 of §1 the sum $F_1P + PF_2$ is not a minimum for all points on the line t. Let P_1 be the minimum point for this sum (see Figure 9.13). Then

---

[1]This notation means that the ellipse consists of those points P for which $PF_1 + PF_2 = 2a$.

$$F_1P_1 + P_1F_2 < 2a$$

But this is equivalent to the inequality (2) and consequently the point P_1 on the line t must lie *inside* the ellipse. But t is a tangent line, so this is impossible. Hence n must bisect $\angle F_1PF_2$.   Q.E.D.

This theorem has an interesting interpretation. If a mirror has the shape of an ellipse, then a ray of light issuing from one of the foci, say F_1, will pass through F_2, the other focus, and in fact, continuing its journey will pass alternately through F_1 and F_2 infinitely often. The reader will find it instructive to draw a large ellipse carefully, and follow the path of a light ray through a number of reflections.

This same theorem is the basis for the construction of whispering galleries. The roof of the gallery is built in the shape of an ellipsoid of revolution, and the tourist is placed at one of the foci. Then any sound that he makes is echoed repeatedly, much to his astonishment. From this phenomenon, we can infer that sound waves are reflected in accordance with the same law as light waves.

The situation is similar for a parabola. For convenience we place the parabola so that the directrix d is a horizontal line, and the focus F lies above the line. Then, as indicated in Figure 9.14, the parabola opens upward and we can speak of points as being above the parabola and below the parabola without being obscure. With these agreements we have

Theorem 3. *If P is on the parabola then $PF = PD$, if P_a is above the parabola then*

$$(3) \qquad P_aF < P_aD,$$

and if P_b is below the parabola then

$$(4) \qquad P_bF > P_bD.$$

Here F is the focus of the parabola, and D is the foot of the perpendicular from the point P to the directrix.

Proof. Let P_a be any point above the parabola (see Figure 9.14). Through P_a draw a line parallel to the directrix and let P_1 be a point of intersection of this line with the parabola. Then $P_aD = P_1D_1$. Further by the definition of a parabola $P_1D_1 = P_1F$. Hence $P_aD = P_1F$. But obviously $P_1F > P_aF$, whence $P_aD > P_aF$ and this is (3).

A similar argument can be used to prove (4) for a point P_b below the parabola, if the line through P_b meets the parabola. We leave the details for the reader, together with the discussion of the case in which the line through P_b parallel to the directrix does not meet the parabola.

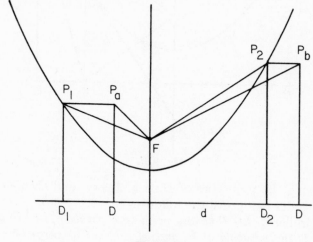

Fig. 9.14

Theorem 4. *Let P be any point on a parabola, and let PD be the segment perpendicular to the directrix at D. Then the bisector of $\angle FPD$ is tangent to the parabola at P.*

Proof. For a parabola $PF = PD$, so the bisector of $\angle FDP$ is the perpendicular bisector of the segment FD (see Figure 9.15). Let t denote this bisector and select any other point P' on t. Then $P'F = P'D > P'D'$ where D' is the foot of the perpendicular from the point P' to the directrix d. But then by theorem 3 the point P' lies below the parabola. Consequently the line t touches the parabola at only one point P, and all other points on t lie on the same side of the parabola. Whence t is tangent to the parabola at P. 						Q.E.D.

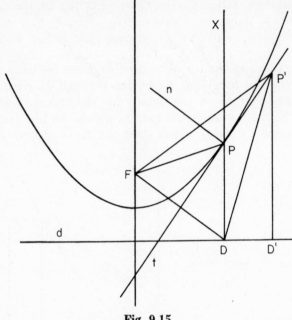

Fig. 9.15

Using the properties of vertical angles, and theorem 4, the reader can prove the following

Corollary. *Let P be any point on a parabola, let t be tangent to the parabola at P, and let n be a line perpendicular to t at P. Then the line n bisects ∠FPX, where PX is a line segment parallel to the axis of the parabola and lying above the parabola* (see Figure 9.15).

In other words a light ray emanating from the focus and striking the surface of a parabolic mirror is reflected parallel to the axis. This principle is basic for the construction of searchlights and reflecting telescopes.

Exercise 2

1. Let l, w, and h denote the length, width, and height of the room in § 2, and suppose the spider is x ft above the floor and the fly is y feet above the floor. Suppose further that, just as in § 2, the spider and fly are on opposite ends of the room each on the vertical bisector of the ends. Find the shortest path from the spider to the fly if $l = 21$, $w = 8$, $h = 10$, $x = 3$, and $y = 6$.

2. Solve the preceding problem if $l = 21$, $w = 12$, $h = 10$, $x = 1$, and $y = 8$.

★**3.** Using the notation and conditions of problem 1, prove that the distance along Path III (Figure 9.9) is less than the distance along Path I if and only if
$$w(w + 2l) < 4xy + 2l(x + y).$$

★**4.** Prove that the distance along Path II is less than the distance along Path I if and only if
$$w(2x + 2y + 2l + w) < 4y(x + l).$$

★**5.** Prove that the distance along Path II is less than the distance along Path III if and only if
$$4x(l + y) + 2w(x + y) < 2lw + w^2.$$

★**6.** A fly wandered into a mathematical museum one hot summer day, and landed on the face of a regular tetrahedron (a solid with four faces, each an equilateral triangle, see Figure 9.16). A spider on an adjoining face

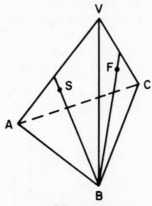

Fig. 9.16

noticed the fly through the transparent material of the model and decided to get better acquainted. What is the length of the shortest path on the surface of the tetrahedron from the spider to the fly if each edge of the tetrahedron is 10 inches, the fly is 1 inch from the edge VC and on the bisector of $\angle VBC$, and the spider is 1 inch from the edge AV and on the bisector of $\angle VBA$?

★7. Suppose that in problem 6 the spider and the fly are x inches from the edges AV and VC respectively, while all other conditions of the problem are the same. Show that the shortest path is across the back face $\triangle AVC$ (Figure 9.16) if and only if $x \leqq 10 - 5\sqrt{3}$, and that under these circumstances the length of the shortest path is $5 + \sqrt{3}x$ inches.

★★8. Let P and Q be given fixed points that lie outside a given fixed circle and suppose further that some tangent line to the circle separates the circle from the two points. Prove that among all polygonal paths PAQ, where A is a point on the circle, the one with the smallest length is the one for which $\angle PAQ$ is bisected by the line from the center of the circle to A.

★★9. Let P be a point inside a given fixed triangle ABC. Investigate the location of the point P so that the sum of its distances from the vertices of the triangle $PA + PB + PC$ will be a minimum. *Hint*: First assume that the angles of the triangle are all less than $120°$, and then apply the result of the preceding problem three times to show that P must be such that $\angle APB = \angle BPC = \angle CPA = 120°$. What is the situation if some angle of the triangle is equal to or greater than $120°$?

★★★10. Given a triangle ABC, we drop from each vertex a line perpendicular to the opposite side. Let P, Q, and R

Fig. 9.17

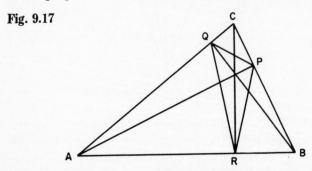

be the intersection points of these perpendiculars with the sides BC, CA, and AB respectively. Then the triangle PQR is by definition the *pedal triangle* of the triangle

ABC. Prove that if all the angles of triangle *ABC* are acute, then the triangle inscribed in triangle *ABC* (one vertex on each side) with the smallest perimeter is the pedal triangle. This is a very difficult problem. For a solution see either (*a*) Rademacher and Toeplitz, *The Enjoyment of Mathematics* (Princeton, N.J.: Princeton University Press, 1957), pp. 28–33, or (*b*) Courant and Robbins, *What Is Mathematics?* (London: Oxford University Press, 1941), pp. 346–351. (See Figure 9.17.)

★4. **The isoperimetric problem.** We have seen in Chapter 8 (problem 4 of exercise 4) that among all rectangles with a given fixed perimeter the one with the largest area is the square. What is the situation if we allow other closed curves with the same perimeter to compete with the rectangle for the honor of enclosing the greatest area? To be specific let the fixed perimeter be 10 units. Then a simple computation for three elementary closed curves reveals:

Closed curve	Side or radius	Area
Equilateral triangle	$\dfrac{10}{3}$	$\dfrac{1}{2}\dfrac{10}{3}\dfrac{\sqrt{3}}{2}\dfrac{10}{3} = 4.811\cdots$
Square	$\dfrac{10}{4}$	$\left(\dfrac{5}{2}\right)^2 = 6.250$
Circle	$\dfrac{10}{2\pi}$	$\pi\left(\dfrac{5}{\pi}\right)^2 = 7.957\cdots$

It appears as though the circle encloses the largest area, for all closed curves with the same perimeter. But of course we have examined only a few of the infinitely many curves. The theorem that the circle does indeed furnish the largest area, is known as the *isoperimetric theorem*.

In proving this theorem we follow the path indicated by Steiner[2] which consists of a large number of individually simple steps.

[2]Jakob Steiner, 1796–1863, a Swiss mathematician, has been called "the greatest geometer since the time of Apollonius." His father was a peasant and the boy had no opportunity to learn reading and writing until the age of fourteen.

A. We recall that a *convex curve* is a curve that is the boundary of a convex region. A region is said to be *convex* if given any two points in the region, the line segment joining those points lies in the region. For example the square, the circle, and the ellipse are all convex curves because they are boundaries of convex regions. The region $\mathcal{R}$ bounded by the curve C of Figure 9.18a is not convex,

Fig. 9.18   (a)   (b)

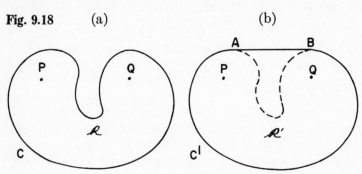

because the line segment joining the points P and Q of that figure, will fall partly outside the region.

We can convert this region $\mathcal{R}$ into a convex region by adding more points to it. We call this process the *convexification* of the region $\mathcal{R}$, if we make this addition efficiently by adding as few points as possible. More accurately we say that $\mathcal{R}'$ is the region obtained by convexifying $\mathcal{R}$ if $\mathcal{R}'$ is the smallest convex region that contains all the points of $\mathcal{R}$. The process of convexifying the region $\mathcal{R}$ of Figure 9.18a is shown in Figure 9.18b. The line segment AB is tangent to the curve C at both end points, and the points included between that segment and the shorter of the two arcs joining A and B have been added to $\mathcal{R}$ to form $\mathcal{R}'$.

Now to begin the proof of the isoperimetric theorem. We consider the set $\mathcal{M}$ of all simple closed curves with a given fixed perimeter L. We select one of these curves C for consideration, and let us suppose first that C bounds a region $\mathcal{R}$ that is not convex. We then replace C by a new curve C'', the boundary of the region $\mathcal{R}'$ obtained by convexifying $\mathcal{R}$. Obviously the area of $\mathcal{R}'$ is greater than or equal to that of $\mathcal{R}$, and furthermore the perimeter L' of C' is less than L, because an arc has been replaced by a line segment (in one or more places).

We next use a magnification to replace the curve C' by a curve C'' similar to C'. The process is indicated graphically in Figure 9.19. We select any point P lying in the

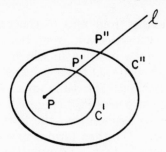

Fig. 9.19

region bounded by C' and let P' be the point of intersection of the curve C' with a ray l issuing from P. We select P'' on l such that the ratio

$$P''P/P'P = L/L'.$$

Then the curve C'' is the curve consisting of all such points P'' obtained in the above manner, as the ray l rotates about the point P through one revolution. It is intuitively obvious that the length of the curve C'' is L/L' times the length of C' and this fact can be given a rigorous proof. Since the curve C' has length L', the curve C'' has length L.

Summarizing the result of our first step, we have proved the following: for any simple closed curve C with perimeter L, that is not convex, we can, by first convexifying and then by magnifying, find a convex curve C'' that has the same perimeter L and encloses a larger area. Thus a nonconvex curve cannot enclose the largest area, among all curves with the same perimeter.

B. We now turn our attention to the convex curves in the set $\mathcal{M}$. We select such a curve and let P be a fixed point on the curve and l a ray through P cutting the curve at a second point Q. This ray divides the region $\mathcal{R}$ into two regions $\mathcal{R}_1$ and $\mathcal{R}_2$, and as the ray rotates in an appropriate direction (see Figure 9.20) the area of $\mathcal{R}_1$ will

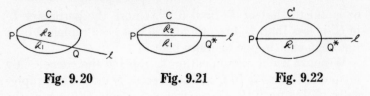

Fig. 9.20   Fig. 9.21   Fig. 9.22

increase continuously from zero to the area of $\mathcal{R}$, while the area of $\mathcal{R}_2$ will decrease from that of $\mathcal{R}$ to zero. Whence there is some position in which l bisects $\mathcal{R}$, *i.e.* there is a point $Q^\star$ such that the line segment $PQ^\star$ divides $\mathcal{R}$ into two regions with the same area. Let us compare the lengths of the two arcs $PQ^\star$ (Figure 9.21) and in order to be definite let us assume that the lower arc is shorter than the upper arc. We then form a new curve C' by removing the upper arc $PQ^\star$, and reflecting the lower arc about the line l (see Figure 9.22). Then C' encloses a region with the same area as C but has a smaller perimeter. Finally magnification, as in step A, leads to a curve C'' with perimeter L that encloses a region of a larger area than C does. Summarizing we have proved that if a line that bisects the area enclosed by the curve does not bisect the perimeter, then that curve does not enclose the largest area. Hence in our search for the curve in the set $\mathcal{M}$ that encloses the largest area we can restrict our attention to those curves that have the property that every line that bisects the area enclosed also bisects the perimeter. We call such lines *diameters*, and we begin to feel that victory is near at hand, when we recall that for a circle each diameter does indeed simultaneously bisect the area and the perimeter.

C. We now select a curve C from the set $\mathcal{M}$ such that each bisector of the area enclosed also bisects the perimeter. Let PQ be one such diameter (Figure 9.23) and let A be any third point on the perimeter. To play safe we can reflect the arc PAQ about the diameter PQ in order to obtain a curve that is symmetric about the line PQ. By the special properties of the original curve, both the area and the perimeter are unchanged.

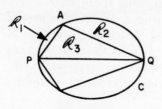

Fig. 9.23

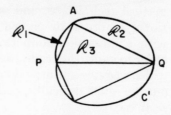

Fig. 9.24

To be specific let A be a point on the upper arc PQ (see Figure 9.23) and suppose that $\angle PAQ \neq 90°$. The sides of the triangle PAQ divide the region above the diameter PQ into three parts which we denote by $\mathcal{R}_1$, $\mathcal{R}_2$, and $\mathcal{R}_3$. Let us imagine that the triangle PAQ has a hinge at A, then by swinging the arms PA and AQ we can alter this triangle to form a right triangle with the same sides PA and AQ, and a *greater area*. During this rotation the regions $\mathcal{R}_1$ and $\mathcal{R}_2$ are also rotated but maintain their shape. Thus the area of the portion above the diameter is *increased* while the perimeter is unchanged. If we carry out this same deformation on the region below the diameter PQ, we are led to a new curve C' (Figure 9.24) that has the same perimeter as C, and encloses a larger area.

Summarizing we have proved that if PQ is a diameter for a curve C, and if A is any point on the curve, then the angle PAQ must be a right angle if the curve is to enclose the greatest area.

Now it is easy to prove that the circle is the only curve with the property that $\angle PAQ = 90°$ for every diameter PQ and every point A on the curve. Whence that curve in $\mathcal{M}$ which encloses the greatest area is the circle. Q.E.D.

★5. A criticism. As attractive as the preceding "proof" of the isoperimetric theorem may be, it contains an error. The reader is invited to reconsider the "proof" carefully and see if he can locate the error for himself.

In the argument of the preceding section, we frequently made appeal to intuition, and it might at first glance appear that the error is in one of these appeals. Actually in such cases we have indeed omitted essential steps of the proof, but these gaps can be filled by the trained mathematical technicians, and our omissions there were intentional in order to prevent marring a beautiful "proof" with a mass of unimportant and distracting detail. In order to assist the reader we make a list of those statements which: (a) are intuitively obvious, (b) can be proved without too much difficulty, and (c) were used in the preceding section.

(1) Any region can be convexified.

(2) If a non-convex region is convexified the perimeter of the boundary is decreased, while the area of the region either remains the same, or is increased.

(3) If a curve is magnified with a magnification ratio K, the perimeter of the curve is multiplied by K and the area enclosed by the curve is multiplied by K^2.

(4) Given a simple closed curve C, and a point P on C, there is a line l through P that bisects the area enclosed by the curve.

(5) Reflection of a closed curve about a line does not change the length of the curve nor the area enclosed by the curve.

(6) The circle is the only curve with the property that for any diameter PQ and any third point A on the curve $\angle PAQ = 90°$.

To repeat, the error of the proof does not lie in any of the above statements.

The error lies in the fact that our "proof" was negative in nature, that is each time we examined a curve in our set $\mathcal{M}$ we decided that if the curve *was not a circle*, then the area enclosed *was not a maximum*. This sounds as though the only possibility left is for the circle to be the curve that does enclose the maximum area. However a little step is needed in order to draw this conclusion and that step is the assertion "the problem has a solution" *i.e.* "*there is a curve in the set $\mathcal{M}$ that encloses the greatest area.*"

In order to see that there really is a gap in the proof, let us consider an analogous theorem and proof, namely,

Theorem (False). *Among all the positive integers* 1 *is the largest.*

"*Proof.*" Select any integer x and compare it with x^2.

If $x \neq 1$, then $x < x^2$, but if $x = 1$, then $x = x^2$. Therefore 1 must be the largest positive integer.

Where is the error in this "proof," which follows exactly the pattern of the "proof" of the isoperimetric theorem? It lies in the assumption that there is such a thing as a largest positive integer.

Of course in the case of the isoperimetric theorem, the problem does have a solution, and this gap can be filled. What is important here is that we examine carefully the logical structure of the proof, and admit that there is a gap that must be filled. The details of how this gap is filled, are not too important.

Exercise 3

1. Prove that for a rectangle, every line that bisects the area, also bisects the perimeter.

2. Is the preceding property true for (a) an equilateral triangle? (b) a regular pentagon? (c) a parallelogram?

★**3.** Consider the region formed by deleting from the interior of a circle those points which lie on some fixed radial line. Show that this region is not convex. On convexification of this region, what happens to the perimeter and the area?

4. Assuming the isoperimetric theorem, prove that if L is the length of any simple closed curve and A is the area of the enclosed region then

$$A \leqq \frac{L^2}{4\pi}$$

with equality only for the circle.

★**5.** Given a fixed area S for the surface of a box (rectangular parallelepiped) prove that the volume V satisfies the inequality $V \leqq (S/6)^{3/2}$ and that the equality sign occurs for the cube. *Hint:* Apply the theorem that the arithmetic mean is greater than or equal to the geometric mean, to the sum $S = 2ab + 2bc + 2ca$.

★**6.** Given a fixed number E for the sum of the lengths of the 12 edges of a box find the maximum volume of the box with E for the sum of the lengths of its edges.

CHAPTER 10

The Theory of Numbers

1. Introduction. We are going to play a game called "The Theory of Numbers" in which only the integers (whole numbers) are used. Whenever we have two integers we can always add them, multiply them, or subtract one from the other, obtaining in each case another integer. But if we try to divide one integer by another, the quotient need not be an integer. For example let the two integers be 5 and 8. Then $5 + 8 = 13$, an integer. Subtraction gives $5 - 8 = -3$, an integer. Multiplication gives $5 \times 8 = 40$, an integer. But division gives $\frac{5}{8}$, not an integer ($\frac{8}{5}$ is also not an integer).

When we insist on using only integers this induces a fundamental change in the algebraic manipulations and gives an entirely new branch of mathematics.

Some equations that are easy to solve with real numbers become difficult or impossible when only integers are to be used. As an example consider the equation

$$(1) \qquad\qquad 7x + 11y = 5.$$

We can find solutions of this equation by taking any number we wish for x and solving for y. Thus if $x = 0$ in (1) then we find that $y = \frac{5}{11}$. If $x = 10$ then (1) gives $70 + 11y = 5$, and hence $y = (5 - 70)/11$ or $y = -\frac{65}{11}$. Likewise we can select any number we wish for y and compute x. Thus if $y = 0$ then (1) yields $x = \frac{5}{7}$, and if $y = 1$, then $x = (5 - 11)/7 = -\frac{6}{7}$. But observe that in all of the solutions obtained so far, at least one of the

160

pair (x, y) is not an integer. If we insist on solutions in which both x and y are integers then it is not so easy to find a solution of (1). It turns out that if $x = 7$ and $y = -4$ then equation (1) is satisfied by this pair of integers. In fact if t is any integer, then the pair of integers

(2)
$$x = 7 - 11t$$
$$y = -4 + 7t$$

satisfies (1). For example if we set $t = 1$ in (2) we obtain the solution $x = -4$, $y = 3$. If we set $t = 2$ we find $x = -15$ and $y = 10$.

To see that (2) is always a solution of (1) we merely replace x and y in (1) by the values given by (2). The computation runs as follows:

$$7x + 11y = 7(7 - 11t) + 11(-4 + 7t)$$
$$= 49 - 77t - 44 + 77t$$
$$= 49 - 44 = 5,$$

for every value of t.

How did we find this solution of (1), and how can we prove that all solutions of (1) are given by (2)? The process is long and somewhat complicated, and we prefer to omit this material. The interested reader can find it in any good book on number theory.[1] We merely wanted to show that *the equation* $7x + 11y = 5$ *is easy to solve when all real numbers are available, but it is not quite so easy to solve when we permit only integers for x and y.*

Our objective in this chapter is to introduce the reader to the Theory of Numbers, and to present some of the interesting results in that field.

2. Definitions. We begin with the definition of factorization.

Definition 1. *The integer d is said to divide the integer a, if there is an integer q (the quotient) such that a = qd. The integer d is also called a divisor or a factor of a, and the expression qd is called a factorization of a.*

[1]See for example Niven and Zuckerman, *An Introduction to the Theory of Numbers* (New York: John Wiley and Sons, Inc., 1960), or B. M. Stewart, *Theory of Numbers* (New York: The Macmillan Co., 1952).

Examples. The number 1 divides any integer. The number zero can be divided by any integer. The integers 7, 11, and 13 are each factors of 1001. In the set 8, 9, 10, 11, 12, 13, 14, 15 no one of the integers is a factor of any of the others in the set.

Theorem 1. *If[2] b divides a, and c divides b, then c divides a.*

Proof. By hypothesis and definition 1, we have $a = q_1 b$ and $b = q_2 c$. Therefore $a = q_1(q_2 c) = (q_1 q_2)c$ and hence by definition 1, c divides a.

We leave as an exercise for the reader the proofs of the following:

Theorem 2. *If d divides a and d divides b, then d divides a + b and d divides a − b.*

Corollary. *If d divides a and d divides b then d divides ma + nb.*

Theorem 3. *If d divides a, then d divides − a, and − d divides a.*

As a matter of convenience, let us consider only the positive integers. Every integer a has at least two factors, itself and one, for we can always write

$$a = 1 \times a \quad \text{and} \quad a = a \times 1,$$

(and it has two more factors if we decide to include as factors − a, and − 1); if it has other factors then a is called *composite.*

Definition 2. *If an integer a has some factor other than ± a and ± 1, then it is said to be composite. If the integer a is greater than 1 and is not composite it is called a prime.*

Examples. As composite numbers we can cite 9, 15, 50, and 7777.

The first twenty primes are 2, 3, 5, 7, 11, 13, 17, 19, 23, 29, 31, 37, 41, 43, 47, 53, 59, 61, 67, and 71.

The reader should examine this sequence of the first twenty primes very carefully, and try to find some law of

[2]Since we study only integers in this chapter, all letters will denote integers unless otherwise stated. Thus in this theorem a, b, and c are integers.

formation. Then using this law of formation he should attempt to predict the next two primes. Without doubt he will fail, because to this day no law or formula giving the primes has ever been discovered. In fact the prime numbers seem to be distributed among the integers in a completely random manner, and this despite the fact that the definition of a prime is clear and specific. It is just this irregularity of the primes that makes number theory so difficult and at the same time so attractive.

Exercise 1

1. Prove theorem 2 and its corollary.

2. Prove that if d divides a and if d does *not* divide b, then d does *not* divide $a + b$, and d does *not* divide $a - b$.

3. Prove theorem 3.

4. Prove that if a is not a prime, then at least one of its factors is less than or equal to $\sqrt{a}$.

5. Use the result of problem 4 to compile a list of primes between 100 and 200. First write down all the numbers from 100 to 200, and remove all multiples of 2 (the even numbers). Then remove all multiples of 3. Then remove all multiples of 5, etc. According to the result of problem 4, we only need to go as far as the largest prime $p \leqq \sqrt{200}$. Thus removing all multiples of 2, 3, 5, 7, 11, and 13, from the list of numbers from 100 to 200 will leave just the primes comprised between 100 and 200. This method is called the sieve of Eratosthenes, because it strains out all of the composite numbers, leaving just the primes.

6. The function $f(x) = x^2 - x + 41$ will give a prime for $x = 1, 2, 3, \cdots, 40$. Test this assertion by trying a few of these values for x. Does this function give a prime when $x = 41$?

7. Find all the prime factors of (a) 1001, (b) 10,001, and (c) 111,111.

8. Prove that any number of the form abc,abc in the decimal system (for example 843,843) is divisible by 13. *Hint:* First prove it is divisible by 1001. What other prime factors must abc,abc always have?

9. Prove that any number of the form ab,cda,bcd in the decimal system is divisible by 137. What other prime factors must such a number always have?

10. Any number of the form aba,bab in the decimal system has at least four distinct prime factors. Find them.

11. Prove that if b divides a giving a quotient q, and if c divides q, then the product bc divides a.

★**12.** Find some of the solutions of $11x + 13y = 3$ where x and y are both integers.

★**13.** Prove that the equation $3x + 6y = 22$ has no solutions in which both x and y are integers.

3. How many primes are there? If we consult a table of primes (or construct one ourselves) and count the number of primes in each interval of 100 we find the results tabulated below.

Interval	1 100	100 200	200 300	300 400	400 500	500 600
Number of primes[3] in that interval	25	21	16	16	17	14

It seems as though the primes are gradually diminishing in frequency, as we go further out among the numbers, although the slight increase in the 400–500 interval over the two previous intervals is somewhat disturbing. As a check we examine intervals of the same length but still further out.

Interval	4000 4100	4100 4200	4200 4300	4300 4400	4400 4500
Number of primes in that interval	15	9	16	9	11

[3]This means that there are 25 prime numbers greater than 1 and less than 100. There are 21 prime numbers greater than 100 and less than 200, etc.

Here indeed is irregularity! About the only assertion that one could risk on the basis of this experimental evidence is the statement that the primes are generally decreasing in frequency, but the decrease is not steady.

One simple question that naturally occurs is this: as we go further and further out among the numbers, do the primes eventually disappear? Or is it possible that no matter how large a number we select, there is always a still larger number that is a prime? Put differently, we can ask is there a *largest* prime P, or is there not?

If there is a largest prime P, such that all numbers greater than P are composite, then we will say that the number of primes is *finite*. In the contrary case, we say that the number of primes is *infinite*. The question whether the number of primes is finite or infinite was answered more than two thousand years ago by Euclid.

Theorem 4. *The number of primes is infinite.*

Proof. We use a proof by contradiction. That is, we assume that the number of primes is finite and by arriving at a contradiction we show that this is impossible, and hence the number of primes is infinite.

Indeed suppose that the number of primes is finite, and let P be the largest prime. Let us look at the number Q defined by

$$Q = P! + 1 = 1 \cdot 2 \cdot 3 \cdot 4 \cdot \cdots \cdot (P-2)(P-1)P + 1.$$

We try to factor Q. Certainly if we try to divide by 2, we find there is a remainder of 1. The same is true if we try to divide by 3. In fact Q can not be divided by any integer less than or equal to P. Thus if Q is a prime it is certainly larger than P, our presumed largest prime. But even if Q is not a prime, any prime factor of Q must itself be larger than P, because none of the numbers less than or equal to P are divisors of Q. Hence in any case the assumption that P is the largest prime, leads to the ridiculous conclusion that there is another prime that is still larger. A contradiction! Q.E.D.

4. Twin primes. Can two consecutive numbers both be primes? For any two adjacent integers, one of them must be even, so that unless the numbers are 2 and 3, the even one will be composite, and they cannot both be primes. Hence 2 and 3 form the only pair of consecutive integers in which both are primes.

What is the situation if the numbers differ by two? A little thought shows that there are pairs n and $n + 2$ that are both primes, for example we have the pairs (3, 5), (11, 13), (41, 43), and (599, 601).

Definition 3. *If the numbers n and $n + 2$ are both primes, they are called twin primes.*

How many pairs of twin primes are there? A survey similar to that made in the preceding section yields the following results.

Interval	1 100	100 200	200 300	300 400	400 500	500 601
Number of twin primes in the interval	7	7	4	2	3	3

Certainly the twin primes are less frequent than the primes, and they also are decreasing in frequency, but not steadily. Are there infinitely many twin primes, or is there only a finite number of such pairs?

Clearly this question on the number of twin primes is just the next question that one would naturally ask after proving that there are infinitely many primes. And yet after a lapse of more than two thousand years since Euclid proved that the number of primes is infinite, this simple question is still unanswered. To this day nobody knows whether the number of twin primes is finite or infinite.

5. Some unsolved problems. We have already met one unsolved problem in number theory, namely the problem of determining whether the number of twin primes is finite or infinite. Here are a few other problems of the same nature.

A. Find a formula $f(n)$ which gives the nth prime.

This problem is so difficult that there is almost no hope of solving it.

B. Find a formula $f(n)$ which gives a prime for each positive integer n. Here we ask less than in *A*, because we are not asking for the nth prime, but just any prime. The formula $f(n) = n^2 - n + 41$ is a good attempt since it gives a prime for $n = 2, 3, 4, \cdots, 40$, but fails when $n = 41$. It can be proved that no polynomial can be such a function. Fermat suggested the formula $f(n) = 2^{2^n} + 1$ which gives a prime for $n = 0, 1, 2, 3,$ and 4, but as Euler showed when $n = 5$, the number obtained is divisible by 641.

C. Tchebychev[4] proved that if $n > 1$, then there is always at least one prime between n and $2n$. But is there always a prime between n^2 and $(n + 1)^2$, for $n > 1$? The conjecture is that this latter assertion is true. But no one has been able to prove it.

D. Are there infinitely many primes p such that $p - 1$ is a perfect square (the square of an integer)? As examples we can cite $5 - 1 = 2^2$, $17 - 1 = 4^2$, $37 - 1 = 6^2$, and $101 - 1 = 10^2$.

E. A famous conjecture due to Goldbach states that every even number $n > 4$ is the sum of two primes. For example $20 = 7 + 13$, $56 = 19 + 37$, and $100 = 53 + 47$. In 1937 I. M. Vinogradov proved that every large odd number is the sum of three primes. Although this is close, it is not the same thing, and Goldbach's conjecture is still unsettled.

F. If the sum of all the divisors of a number n is equal to $2n$, then the number is called a perfect number. For example the divisors of 6 are 1, 2, 3, and 6, and $1 + 2 + 3 + 6 = 12 = 2 \times 6$. Therefore 6 is a perfect number. The same is true for 28 since $1 + 2 + 4 + 7 + 14 + 28 = 56 = 2 \times 28$. Euclid proved that if $2^k - 1$ is a prime then the number $n = 2^{k-1}(2^k - 1)$ is a perfect number. Euler proved that if n is an *even* perfect number then $n = 2^{k-1}(2^k - 1)$ where $2^k - 1$ is a prime. Are there any

[4] P. L. Tchebychev, 1821–1894, was one of the leading Russian mathematicians of that period.

odd perfect numbers? No one has ever found an odd perfect number, but also no one has been able to prove that there aren't any.

In every field of mathematics there are important and interesting unsolved problems. The energetic and bright young mathematician need not complain that there is nothing new for him to discover in mathematics. The main trouble is that in most branches of mathematics the open questions do not appear until after several years of study. But Number Theory is the exception, as we have just seen. In this branch of mathematics it takes only a few basic concepts (covered here in 8 pages) to allow us to state 6 unsolved problems. The solution of any one of the problems A, B, C, D, E, or F would bring to the solver instant world-wide recognition.

Exercise 2

1. Which of the following numbers are primes?
        (*a*) $3! + 1$,   (*b*) $5! + 1$,   (*c*) $7! + 1$.

2. Use problem 2 of exercise 1 to prove that if $1 < d \leq P$, then d does not divide $P! + 1$.

3. List the sets of twin primes between 50 and 100.

4. Check Goldbach's conjecture by representing as the sum of two primes each of the numbers (*a*) 40, (*b*) 62, (*c*) 84, and (*d*) 108.

5. Show that 496 is a perfect number.

6. Find three more primes p such that $p - 1$ is a perfect square.

7. The prime 3 has the property that it is one less than a perfect square (that is, $p + 1$ is a perfect square). Prove that this is the only prime that has that property.

★**8.** Prove that every odd prime is the difference of two squares, and in just one way. Find the two squares for the primes 11, 17, and 29. Is the same assertion true for the composite number 21?

6. The greatest common divisor. Let us examine the pair of numbers 156 and 192 for factors. Since both numbers are even we find at once that 2 is a factor of both numbers. We call 2 a *common factor* or *common divisor* for 156 and 192. Dividing both numbers by 2 we obtain 78 and 96. Since both are even we can again divide by 2 obtaining the pair 39 and 48. Inspection shows that 3 divides both of these numbers, yielding 13 and 16. This last pair consists of numbers so small that we can see at a glance that they have no common divisor other than 1.

Returning to our original pair, we observe that we could divide each by 2, 2, and 3, and hence by the product 12 (see problem 11 exercise 1). If we search for other common divisors we will find that the list 1, 2, 4, 6, and 12 gives all of the positive common divisors of 156 and 192. Notice that every one of the common divisors, is a divisor of 12, the greatest one in the set. This suggests that we call 12 the *greatest common divisor* of 156 and 192.

Definition 4. *Given two integers a and b, the positive integer D is called the greatest common divisor of a and b if*:

(1) *D divides a and D divides b*,

(2) *Any other divisor of a and b also divides D*.

In this definition of the greatest common divisor (g.c.d.), part (1) is the "common" part, D divides both a and b; and part (2) is the "greatest" part, any other divisor of a and b divides D. If the two numbers are relatively small (say less than a million) it is intuitively obvious that they have a greatest common divisor, that can be found by trying all possible factors. However for large numbers this is not obvious and we need

Theorem 5. *Every pair of numbers has a greatest common divisor.*

The proof of this theorem is a little complicated and so we omit it.

Definition 5. *Two numbers are said to be relatively prime, if their greatest common divisor is 1.*

Examples. The greatest common divisor of 48 and 81 is 3. For the numbers 707 and 2002 the greatest common divisor is 7. The numbers 10,001 and 111,111 are relatively prime.

Theorem 6. *Every integer can be factored into a product of primes and except for changes in the order of the primes this factorization is unique.*

Examples.

$$1001 = 7 \times 11 \times 13 = 11 \times 7 \times 13 = 13 \times 7 \times 11 = \cdots$$
$$48 = 2^4 \times 3 = 2^3 \times 3 \times 2 = 2^2 \times 3 \times 2^2 = \cdots.$$

The proof of theorem 6 depends on theorem 5 and is just a matter of technique, hence there is no great loss if we omit the proof of this theorem.[5]

Theorem 6 supplies a systematic way of finding the g.c.d. (greatest common divisor) of two numbers. We merely factor each number into a product of primes, and then look for the primes common in both factorizations. For example to find the g.c.d. of 29,328 and 38,376 we have on factoring:

$$29,328 = 2^4 \times 3 \times 13 \times 47,$$
$$38,376 = 2^3 \times 3^2 \times 13 \times 41.$$

Therefore the g.c.d. is $2^3 \times 3 \times 13 = 312$.

Exercise 3

1. Find the g.c.d. for each of the following pairs of numbers:
(a) 275 and 325,
(b) 1243 and 3390,
(c) 2988 and 3096,
(d) 17,765 and 28,014,
(e) 6262 and 5757,
(f) 12,100 and 20,806.

2. Suppose that D is the g.c.d. of a and b and that $a/D = q_1$ and $b/D = q_2$. Prove that q_1 and q_2 are relatively prime.

3. Generalize the definition of the g.c.d. to the g.c.d. of three numbers. What is the g.c.d. for the three numbers 48, 72, and 78?

4. Prove that if c^2 is the square of an even integer then c^2 must be divisible by 4.

5. Use the result of problem 4 to prove that $4X + 2$ is never a square for any integer X.

[5]The proof can be found in any book on the theory of numbers.

★7. Pythagorean triples. The Pythagorean Theorem from plane geometry states that if x, y, and z are the sides and hypotenuse of a right triangle then

(3) $$x^2 + y^2 = z^2.$$

Although it is seldom mentioned, the converse theorem is also true: that if x, y, and z are positive numbers satisfying (3) then the triangle, with these numbers as lengths of the sides, is a right triangle.

It is natural to look for right triangles for which all three of the sides have integer lengths. A brief search reveals that $9 + 16 = 25$ or $3^2 + 4^2 = 5^2$ and hence one such triangle has sides 3, 4, and 5. Indeed this right triangle has been known for over two thousand years. Once we have found such a triangle, we can find infinitely many by using similar triangles. If we multiply each side of this triangle by 2, we get the right triangle with sides 6, 8, and 10, and if we multiply each side by 3 we have a right triangle with sides 9, 12, and 15. In general if $x = a$, $y = b$, and $z = c$ are three integers that satisfy (3) and if k is any integer, then the integers ka, kb, and kc satisfy (3). Conversely if the set (a, b, c) satisfies (3) and they have a common factor k, then the set obtained by dividing through by k will also satisfy (3).

Our objective is to find all sets of positive integers (a, b, c) which satisfy (3).

Definition 6. *If $x = a$, $y = b$, and $z = c$ are positive integers satisfying (3) then the set (a, b, c) is called a Pythagorean triple. If the numbers a, b, and c have no common factor greater than 1, then the set (a, b, c) is called a primitive Pythagorean triple.*

Examples. The set $(3, 4, 5)$ is a primitive Pythagorean triple. The set $(15, 20, 25)$ is a Pythagorean triple, but it is not primitive, because the numbers have the g.c.d. 5.

We are going to find formulas that will give all sets of primitive Pythagorean triples. This in turn will give all Pythagorean triples by multiplying by a suitable constant k. Finding all sets of primitive Pythagorean triples is somewhat complicated, and the logical path is hard to follow if we do not know where we are going. So let us jump ahead for a few moments and examine our destination.

If we square $t^2 - 1$ we obtain $t^4 - 2t^2 + 1$. A sharp eye will observe that if we add $(2t)^2 = 4t^2$ to this quantity we will just change the sign of the middle term, and get $t^4 + 2t^2 + 1$, and this is the square of $t^2 + 1$. Consequently if we set

$$(4) \qquad a = t^2 - 1, \quad b = 2t, \quad c = t^2 + 1$$

then

$$a^2 + b^2 = (t^2 - 1)^2 + (2t)^2 = t^4 - 2t^2 + 1 + 4t^2$$
$$= t^4 + 2t^2 + 1 = (t^2 + 1)^2.$$

Hence

$$(5) \qquad a^2 + b^2 = c^2.$$

Consequently for each integer t, the equation set (4) generates a Pythagorean triple (a, b, c). This is wonderful! But is it the best that we can do? A careful inspection of the process suggests that the "1" in equation set (4) can be replaced by a variable quantity denoted by s^2. Then equation set (4) will be replaced by

$$(6) \qquad a = t^2 - s^2, \quad b = 2ts, \quad c = t^2 + s^2.$$

Does the set (6) generate a Pythagorean triple when t and s are integers? Let us try it out! We find that

$$a^2 + b^2 = (t^2 - s^2)^2 + (2ts)^2$$
$$= t^4 - 2t^2s^2 + s^4 + 4t^2s^2$$
$$= t^4 + 2t^2s^2 + s^4 = (t^2 + s^2)^2 = c^2.$$

It certainly does!

As a wild guess, we might conjecture that all primitive Pythagorean triples can be obtained from equation (6) by a proper selection of integers for t and s. It turns out that this guess is correct. Now that our destination (equation (6)) is clear, let us return to the beginning and follow the logical path that brings us to equation (6). The work is complicated so we break it into four steps.

1. Assume that (a, b, c) is a primitive Pythagorean triple and hence

$$(5) \qquad a^2 + b^2 = c^2.$$

Any common factor of a and b must be a common factor of c, so by the primitivity a and b must be relatively prime. A similar argument shows that a and c are relatively prime, and b and c are relatively prime.

It follows from this that a and b cannot both be even. They cannot both be odd because if they were we could write $a = 2A + 1$, $b = 2B + 1$ and therefore

$$(3) \qquad \begin{aligned} a^2 + b^2 &= (2A + 1)^2 + (2B + 1)^2 \\ &= 4A^2 + 4A + 1 + 4B^2 + 4B + 1 \\ &= 4X + 2 \\ &= c^2 \end{aligned}$$

where $X = A^2 + B^2 + A + B$. But then c^2 would be an integer that is divisible by 2 and not by 4. But c^2 being a square this is impossible (see problem 5 of exercise 3). Hence for a primitive Pythagorean triple (a, b, c) one of the first two numbers must be odd and the other even.

2. Let us agree to let a represent the odd side, and b the even side. From equation (3) we write

$$(7) \qquad b^2 = c^2 - a^2 = (c - a)(c + a).$$

These two factors are integers, let us name them X and Y, *i.e.* we set

$$c + a = Y,$$
and
$$c - a = X.$$

Adding and subtracting these two equations gives,

$$(8) \qquad c = \frac{Y + X}{2} \quad \text{and} \quad a = \frac{Y - X}{2}$$

and equation (7) gives

$$(9) \qquad b^2 = XY.$$

Since c is an integer, equation (8) tells us that X and Y must be either both even, or both odd, in order that the sum be divisible by 2. On the other hand b is even, so by equation (9) at least one of X and Y is even. Consequently both are even.

3. Since X and Y are both even we can represent them

as $2u$ and $2v$ respectively where u and v are integers. When we set $X = 2u$ and $Y = 2v$ equation set (8) becomes

(10) $$c = v + u \quad \text{and} \quad a = v - u,$$

and (9) becomes

(11) $$b^2 = 4uv.$$

4. We assert that u and v are relatively prime, because by (10) any common factor of u and v would also be a common factor of c and a, and we have already proved that a and c are relatively prime. But then if u and v are relatively prime it is easy to see from (11) that each must be a perfect square. We set $u = s^2$ and $v = t^2$ and we are prepared to retrace our steps. Indeed (10) gives $c = t^2 + s^2$, $a = t^2 - s^2$, and (11) gives $b = 2st$. We have proved

Theorem 7. *If (a, b, c) is a primitive Pythagorean triple then there are relative prime integers s and t such that*

(6) $$\begin{aligned} a &= t^2 - s^2, \\ b &= 2ts, \\ c &= t^2 + s^2. \end{aligned}$$

But these are just the formulas we are seeking. For if we select any pair of integers t and s, the equations (6) do give us a Pythagorean triple because as we have already seen when we use (6) we find:

$$a^2 + b^2 = (t^2 - s^2)^2 + (2ts)^2 = t^4 - 2t^2s^2 + s^4 + 4t^2s^2$$
$$= t^4 + 2t^2s^2 + s^4 = (t^2 + s^2)^2 = c^2.$$

Of course the Pythagorean triple may not be primitive. We have seen that s and t must be relatively prime in order to obtain a primitive triple. But if s and t are both odd then a, b, and c will all be even. It can be proved that if one of the numbers s and t is odd and the other is even, and if they are relatively prime then the equation set (6) does give a primitive Pythagorean triple.

Example. Set $t = 3$, $s = 1$ in equation set (6). Then $a = 3^2 - 1^2 = 8$, $b = 2 \times 3 \times 1 = 6$, and $c = 3^2 + 1 = 10$. The numbers $(8, 6, 10)$ form a Pythagorean triple as predicted because $64 + 36 = 100$. However the set is not primitive.

★8. Fermat's last theorem. In the preceding section we found that there were infinitely many sets of integers satisfying the equation $x^2 + y^2 = z^2$. In fact we found formulas (theorem 7) which gave all such primitive sets. Naturally the next question is: find all the sets of integers for which $x^3 + y^3 = z^3$. It was just this question that occurred to Fermat as he was reading his copy of Bachet's *Diophantus*. We do not know how long Fermat worked at this problem, but we do know that in his opinion he proved that if the exponent n is greater than 2, then the equation $x^n + y^n = z^n$ has no solution with x, y, and z all positive integers. For he wrote in the margin of the book the following note:

"On the contrary it is impossible to separate a cube into two cubes, a fourth power into two fourth powers, or generally any power above the second into powers of the same degree. I have discovered a truly remarkable proof which this margin is too narrow to contain."

We have no hint how Fermat proved this theorem, and for the past 300 years many of the leading mathematicians have sought in vain to reconstruct Fermat's lost proof, or to find one of their own. No one has succeeded. In 1770 Euler managed to prove that there are no solutions when $n = 3$, Legendre and Dirichlet proved that there are no solutions when $n = 5$, and Kummer settled the cases $n = 11$ and $n = 13$. By now it has been proved that there are no solutions of $x^n + y^n = z^n$ in positive integers, for an extremely large number of values of n, but the proof for all n is still lacking.

This then is Fermat's last theorem. It is not really a theorem, because it is not yet proved. Some mathematicians feel Fermat must have made an error in his work. But in all of Fermat's writings not a single error has been discovered so far, so perhaps he really had a valid proof. What a pity the margin of his book was so narrow!

Exercise 4

1. Prove that if $x = a$, $y = b$, and $z = c$ satisfy (1) then

$x = ka$, $y = kb$, and $z = kc$ also satisfy (1).

2. If $a^2 + b^2 = c^2$ and k divides a and c, prove that k divides b.

3. Show that $(10, 24, 26)$ is a Pythagorean triple. Is it primitive?

4. What values should we take for t and s in equation (6) to generate the Pythagorean triple $(3, 4, 5)$; for the triple $(9, 40, 41)$?

5. Find two sets of positive integers that solve the equation

$$x^3 + y^3 = z^2.$$

★**6.** Prove that for any positive integer z the equation
$$x^2 - y^2 = z^3$$
has at least one set of solutions with x and y positive integers.

CHAPTER 11

Permutations and Combinations

1. Two examples. This chapter is devoted to counting. Although "counting" may sound trivial and dull, it can be rather complicated as the reader will soon discover from the problems in the exercise lists. One of the difficulties in counting is the formation of a clear picture of the objects that are being counted. The following two examples appear to be identical and we might at first glance expect the same answer for both. However a little thought reveals that they are fundamentally different.

Example 1. How many three-letter arrangements can be made from the four letters A, B, C, and D if repetitions of a letter in a given arrangement are not allowed?

Example 2. Four points A, B, C, and D are given in a plane, with no three on a straight line. How many different triangles can be drawn using these points as vertices?

For brevity we call each three-letter arrangement, a *word*. In solving the first problem the words ABC, BAC, and CAB are all admissible, and must be regarded as distinct in our counting. However, in the second problem the triangles ABC, BAC, and CAB are all the same and should not be regarded as distinct in our counting.

We now have a clear picture of the objects to be counted in each case. After a general theory has been formulated these two problems will be trivial. But until we have such a theory, the simplest procedure is to make a list of the objects and count them directly. Further it is instructive to do this because it suggests the theory, and helps us to understand it.

In solving the first problem we select first the three letters A, B, and C and then make all possible arrangements of these three letters. We then do the same with

177

letters A, B, and D. Continuing in this systematic way, we eventually arrive at the list of Table I, that contains 24 words. Therefore the answer to the first problem is 24.

Words without D	Words without C	Words without B	Words without A
ABC	ABD	ACD	BCD
ACB	ADB	ADC	BDC
BAC	BAD	CAD	CBD
BCA	BDA	CDA	CDB
CAB	DAB	DAC	DBC
CBA	DBA	DCA	DCB

Table I

If we turn to the second problem we notice at once that all six of the words in the first column represent one and the same triangle. Similarly for each of the other columns. Whence using vertices from among the four points A, B, C, and D one can draw four different triangles, one for each column in Table I.

In problems similar to the first one, the objects counted are called *permutations*, while those in the second problem are called *combinations*. To be exact we state:

Definition 1. *Suppose that in the arrangement of k items selected from a set of n different items, the order of arrangement is important, so that different arrangements of the same set of k items are regarded as different. In this case each arrangement is called a permutation. The number of different permutations of n things taken k at a time is denoted by the symbol $P(n, k)$.*

Definition 2. *Suppose that in the arrangement of k items selected from a set of n different items, the order of arrangement is not important so that different arrangements of the same set of k items are regarded as being the same. In this case each arrangement is called a combination. The number of different combinations of n things taken k at a time is denoted by the symbol $C(n, k)$.*

We use the above examples to illustrate our new terminology and notation.

The number of different three letter words that can be

formed from the four letters A, B, C, and D is the number of *permutations* of 4 things taken 3 at a time, and by direct counting $P(4, 3) = 24$.

The number of different triangles that can be formed with vertices selected from four points A, B, C, D in general position, is the number of *combinations* of 4 things taken 3 at a time, and by direct counting $C(4, 3) = 4$.

2. A fundamental principle. We observe that in making a three letter word from the four given letters, we first selected one of the letters, then selected another from those remaining and so on. In order to assist us in counting the number of different ways in which this can be done we need the

Fundamental Principle. *If one position can be filled in p different ways, and after it has been filled in any one of these ways, a second position can be filled in q different ways then the two positions can be filled in sequence in pq different ways.*

For example, if the president of a certain company can be selected from a list of four men, and his secretary is to be selected from seven women, in how many ways can these two offices be filled? Here $p = 4$, and $q = 7$, and by the fundamental principle the number of ways is $pq = 4 \times 7 = 28$. Of course if the secretary is chosen first then $p = 7$ and $q = 4$, but the answer is still the same.

Proof of the fundamental principle. Let A_1, A_2, ..., A_p denote the p different ways in which the first position can be filled, and let B_1, B_2, ..., B_q denote the q different ways in which the second position can be filled. Naturally A_3B_5 denotes a sequence in which the first position A is filled in the third way, and the second position B is filled in the fifth way. Then the number of different ways in which the two positions can be filled is the number of entries in the rectangular array

$$
\begin{array}{ccccc}
A_1B_1 & A_1B_2 & A_1B_3 & \cdots & A_1B_q \\
A_2B_1 & A_2B_2 & A_2B_3 & \cdots & A_2B_q \\
A_3B_1 & A_3B_2 & A_3B_3 & \cdots & A_3B_q \\
\cdot & \cdot & \cdot & \cdots & \cdot \\
A_pB_1 & A_pB_2 & A_pB_3 & \cdots & A_pB_q
\end{array}
$$

Since this rectangular array has p lines and q columns it contains pq elements altogether. Q.E.D.

It is obvious that this general principle can be extended to a sequence of any number of different positions.

Example 1. A young lady has 4 different sweaters, 6 different skirts, and 3 different pairs of shoes. In how many different ways can she dress?

Solution. By the fundamental principle she can select a sweater and a skirt in $4 \times 6 = 24$ different ways, and then with each of these ways select her shoes in any one of 3 different ways obtaining $24 \times 3 = 72$ different outfits. This is just the product $4 \times 6 \times 3 = 72$.

Exercise 1

1. The chief designer for a large automobile company is considering 4 different radiator grilles, 2 different styles of headlights, and 5 different rear fender designs. With respect to these items alone how many different style cars can be made?

2. A man can travel from Princeton, New Jersey, to New York in any one of 4 different ways, and can proceed from there to Cambridge, Massachusetts, in any one of 7 different ways. In how many ways can he make the trip from Princeton to Cambridge? In how many ways can he make the round trip?

3. How many numbers are there between 100 and 1000 for which each digit is odd? How many of these are between 100 and 500?

4. How many three-letter words can be formed from the letters of the English alphabet if the middle letter must be one of the vowels A, E, I, O, and U, while the first and last letters must be consonants and the letter Q is not to be used?

5. A college freshman is to have a program of four courses. He is to take either one of 2 English courses, a beginning course in any one of 4 different foreign languages, any one of 3 different mathematics courses, and any one of 4 different science courses. How many different programs of study are possible?

6. Having selected his program, the student in problem 5, finds that there are 7 different sections of English (all meeting at different times), 3 different sections of the foreign language, 5 different sections of mathematics, and 3 different sections of the science course. Assuming there are no conflicts in time, how many different schedules are possible?

7. A large TV set with an outdoor antenna receives 13 channels, while a smaller set in the den can be tuned only to the 4 local channels. In how many different ways can these two sets be receiving programs?

8. A manufacturer makes shirts in 5 different patterns, each in 7 different neck sizes, and each neck size with 3 different sleeve lengths. How many different shirts must a store stock in order to carry a complete line of these shirts?

9. How many different divisors[1] are there for the number $2 \times 3 \times 5 \times 7 = 210$? Note that 1 and 210 are divisors. How many are there for the number $2^3 \times 3^2 \times 5^2 = 1800$?

10. A true-false examination has 10 statements which the student may mark T or F. In how many different ways can the student guess at the answers?

3. Permutations. Using the fundamental principle it is easy to prove

Theorem 1. *The number of permutations of n things taken k at a time is given by the formula*

(1) $$\boxed{P(n, k) = n(n-1)(n-2) \cdots (n-k+1).}$$

Proof. For simplicity we can think of the n things as n different letters of the alphabet, and the permutations as the various k letter words that can be formed from the n letters without repetitions.

The letter in the first position can be selected in any one of n ways. After this selection there are only $n-1$ letters left from which to choose the second letter. By the fundamental principle the first two letters can be chosen in

[1]See Chapter 10 for the definition of a divisor.

$n(n - 1)$ different ways. In each case after selection of the first two letters there are $n - 2$ letters left for the third letter of the word. Thus the first three letters can be selected in $n(n - 1)(n - 2)$ different ways. Continuing in this way the number of k letter words that can be formed is the product of k factors, where the first is n, and each is one less than the preceding one, that is, $n(n - 1)(n - 2) \cdots (n - k + 1)$.   Q.E.D.

We observe that by using the factorial notation (explained in Chapter 2) we can write formula (1) in another way:

$$P(n, k) = n(n - 1)(n - 2) \cdots$$
$$\times (n - k + 1) \frac{(n - k)(n - k - 1)(n - k - 2) \cdots 2 \cdot 1}{(n - k)(n - k - 1)(n - k - 2) \cdots 2 \cdot 1}$$

$$(2) \qquad P(n, k) = \frac{n!}{(n - k)!}.$$

Example 1. Solve example 1 of § 1.

Solution. We are to compute the number of three letter words that can be made from the letters A, B, C, and D, and this is just the number of permutations of 4 things taken 3 at a time. By (1) we find that

$$P(4, 3) = 4 \cdot 3 \cdot 2 = 24.$$

This answer agrees with the one obtained by counting the entries in Table I.

Example 2. First, second, third, and fourth prizes are to be awarded in a beauty contest in which 16 very pretty girls are entered. In how many different ways can the prizes be awarded?

Solution. $P(16, 4) = 16 \cdot 15 \cdot 14 \cdot 13 = 43,680.$

No wonder the judges are either gray-headed or bald!

4. Combinations. We can use the formula for the number of permutations to prove

Theorem 2. *The number of combinations of n things taken k at a time is given by the formula*

$$(3) \qquad \boxed{C(n, k) = \frac{n!}{k!(n - k)!}.}$$

Proof. We apply the fundamental principle to the following sequence of acts: (A) select k of the n objects, (B) take all possible permutations of the k objects selected. The first act is merely the selection of a combination of k things and can be done in $C(n, k)$ different ways. The second act is a permutation of k things taken k at a time and can be done in $P(k, k)$ different ways. But the sequence of the two acts gives the number of different permutations of n things taken k at a time, or $P(n, k)$. By the fundamental principle

$$(4) \qquad C(n, k)P(k, k) = P(n, k).$$

But by (1) $P(k, k) = k!$. Using this in (4) gives

$$C(n, k) = P(n, k)/k! .$$

From equation (2) we have $P(n, k) = n!/(n - k)!$ Consequently we see that

$$C(n, k) = \frac{n!}{k!(n - k)!},$$

and this is formula (3).   Q.E.D.

We notice from formula (3) that the number of combinations of n things taken k at a time is the same as the binominal coefficient $\binom{n}{k}$ introduced in Chapter 2.

Example 1. Solve example 2 of § 1.

Solution. We are to compute the number of triangles with vertices among 4 given points, and this is just the number of combinations of 4 things taken 3 at a time. By (3) we find that

$$C(4, 3) = \frac{4!}{3!1!} = \frac{4 \cdot 3 \cdot 2 \cdot 1}{3 \cdot 2 \cdot 1 \cdot 1} = 4.$$

Example 2. How many different poker hands are possible? A poker hand consists of 5 cards dealt from a deck of 52 cards.

Solution. The arrangement of the given cards in the hand is unimportant, so this is a problem on combinations. We want the number of combinations of 52 things taken 5 at a time. By formula (3)

$$C(52, 5) = \frac{52!}{5!47!} = \frac{52 \cdot 51 \cdot 50 \cdot 49 \cdot 48}{5 \cdot 4 \cdot 3 \cdot 2 \cdot 1} = 2,598,960.$$

Exercise 2

1. Compute $C(5, 2)$ and $C(5, 3)$.

2. Compute $C(10, 3)$ and $C(10, 7)$.

★3. The preceding problems illustrated the fact that $C(n, k) = C(n, n-k)$. Prove that this is always true. Is there a combinatorial reason for this equality?

4. How many three letter words can be made using the first 10 letters of the alphabet, if no letter is repeated in any one word. How many, using all the letters of the alphabet?

5. Three flags are to be displayed on a vertical flagpole in order to transmit a message from one boat to another by a prearranged code. If the three flags can be selected from 10 different flags, how many different messages can be transmitted?

6. Two friends agree to meet in the lobby of the theatre, but forget to specify which theatre. If the town has 7 theatres, in how many different ways can they miss each other? In how many different ways can they meet?

7. How many triangles are formed by 6 lines in the plane if no two are parallel and no three are concurrent? Note that some triangles may be inside others. Generalize this problem to n lines.

8. How many fraternity names can be made using the letters of the Greek alphabet (there are 24 letters) if the name consists of three letters and no repetitions are allowed? How many if repetitions are allowed?

9. In how many ways can 8 soldiers be divided into scouting parties with four soldiers in each? In how many ways can the 8 soldiers be divided into two scouting parties if each party has at least one soldier?

10. Given 10 points in space with no 4 lying in the same plane, how many different planes are there containing 3 of the given points? Generalize this problem to n points.

11. A soldier has pictures of 9 different pretty girls

but only space for pinning up 5. In how many ways can he select the ones to pin up?

In problems 12 through 17 solve for n.

12. $P(n, 4) = 1680$.
13. $P(n + 1, 3) = 14C(n, 2)$.
★**14.** $P(n, 4) = 36C(n + 1, 3)$.
★**15.** $5P(n, 3) = 2P(n - 1, 4)$.
★**16.** $21C(n, 3) = 4C(n + 1, 4)$.
★**17.** $8C(n, 4) = C(2n, 3)$.
★★**18.** Solve for n and k, the pair of equations
$$P(n, k) = 840, \qquad C(n, k) = 35.$$
★★**19.** Solve for n and k the pair of equations
$$P(n, k) = 2730, \qquad C(n, k) = 455.$$
★**20.** Find two different solutions for the equation
$$P(n, 3) = k!.$$

5. More difficult problems. We have developed a formula for the number of permutations of n things taken k at a time, and another formula for the number of combinations of n things taken k at a time. These formulas will handle the standard problems of counting. We could continue to develop more formulas to meet more complex situations, but we prefer to avoid further formulas. It is better to treat each problem individually on its own merits as indicated in the following examples.

Example 1. In how many ways can 5 people line up for a group picture if 2 of the 5 are not on speaking terms and refuse to stand next to each other?

Solution. Let A, B, C, D, and E denote the various members of the group and suppose that A and B are the cantankerous ones. If we ignore the wishes of A and B, then the number of ways of lining up is just the number of permutations of 5 things taken 5 at a time and is $5! = 120$. We must subtract the number of permutations in which A and B stand side by side. We denote the A, B set by a single letter X, and observe that the number of permutations of the set X, C, D, E is just $4! = 24$. In these permutations A and B stand next to each other. But we can interchange A and B in each such permutation. For example $CDABE$ and $CDBAE$ are both permutations in which A and B are side by side. Therefore the total number of permutations with A and B next to each other is $2 \times 4!$, and hence the number of ways of lining up for a photograph with A and B separated is

$$5! - 2 \times 4! = 120 - 48 = 72.$$

Example 2. There are 10 boys and 6 girls at the tennis courts. In how many ways can a doubles game be arranged if each side consists of a boy and a girl?

Solution. The two boys can be selected in $C(10, 2) = 10 \times 9/2$ different ways. Similarly the two girls can be selected in $C(6, 2) = 6 \times 5/2$ different ways. After the four have been selected to play, one of the boys may select either of the two girls for his partner. Hence the number of ways of arranging a doubles game is

$$2 \times \frac{10 \times 9}{2} \times \frac{6 \times 5}{2} = 1350.$$

Example 3. Find the number of permutations that can be formed with the letters of the word Nevada.

Solution. First we regard the two a's as different and in order to observe the difference we might paint one red and the other blue. Then the number of permutations of these 6 letters all different is $6!$. Now with any one permutation in which the red a appears first there is a similar permutation with the red a and the blue a interchanged, so that the blue a appears first. When the paint is removed these two permutations are indistinguishable. Hence only half of the $6!$ permutations are different and the answer is $6!/2 = 360$.

Suppose that we are to find the number of permutations of the letters of the word almanac. If the a's are all different then there are $7!$ such permutations. But the 3 a's can be permuted $3!$ ways in each such arrangement, so that if the a's are indistinguishable then there are only $7!/3! = 840$ permutations.

Example 4. How many different sums of money can be made using a penny, a nickel, a dime, a quarter, and a half dollar?

Solution. We have 5 coins, so taking just one coin there are $C(5, 1) = 5$ different sums. Using two coins there are $C(5, 2) = 10$ different sums. In general if we use k of the coins, the number of different sums is the number of combinations of 5 things taken k at a time. Then the total number of possible sums of money is

$$
\begin{aligned}
& C(5, 1) + C(5, 2) + C(5, 3) + C(5, 4) + C(5, 5) \\
= \quad & 5 \quad + \quad 10 \quad + \quad 10 \quad + \quad 5 \quad + \quad 1 \quad = 31.
\end{aligned}
$$

We leave for the reader the task of proving that two different selections of coins have different sums.

Exercise 3

1. In how many ways can 6 persons, A, B, C, D, E, and F line up for a picture if A and B refuse to stand next to each other, while C and D insist on standing next to each other?

2. Do problem 1 under the assumption that A, B, and C insist on being together with B always between A and C.

3. In how many ways can 4 boys and 4 girls stand in line if the boys and the girls are to alternate in line?

4. There are 7 boys and 4 girls at a dance. In how many ways can they form couples to dance if all of the girls have partners?

5. Do problem 4, if one couple is going steady and refuses to split.

6. Find the number of different permutations of the letters in each of the following words: (a) monotone, (b) banana, (c) ukulele, (d) Tennessee, and (e) Mississippi.

7. Find the number of different weights (greater than zero) that can be formed using weights of 1, 2, 4, 8, 16, and 32 lbs.

8. Find the number of different poker hands with exactly two aces that can be obtained from a regulation 52 card deck.

9. In the design of a four motor plane consideration must be given to the possibility that some of the engines may fail to operate. How many different design conditions must be considered if at least one engine is running and if symmetrical situations are regarded as the same?

★10. In how many different ways can 4 people be seated around a circular table? Two ways are counted as different only if someone has a different neighbor in the two arrangements. Generalize to find a formula for n people.

★11. Two tables of bridge are to be arranged among 8 players. In how many different ways can this be done if two arrangements are regarded as the same when each player has the same partner, and the same pair of opponents?

★12. In how many different ways can the opening day baseball games be arranged in a league consisting of 8 teams, if we disregard the place where the game is played?

Find the number of ways, if at least one team from each pair is playing on its home ground, and the location of the game is regarded as important.

★★13. Let each of p points lying on a line be joined by line segments to each of q points lying on a second line parallel to the first. Find the number of points of intersection of these line segments that lie in the strip bounded by the given parallel lines, if no three of the segments are concurrent.

★14. Given n points on a circle, all chords with these points as end points are drawn. If no three chords are concurrent find the number of intersection points of these chords in the circle.

★15. Given n points in a plane, we join them by straight lines in all possible ways. Assuming that no two lines are parallel and no three are concurrent find the number of points of intersection of these lines not counting the originally given points.

★16. Given n points in a plane with k of them on a straight line but the others in general position, find the number of straight lines that can be formed by joining pairs of these points.

★17. A rectangle is cut by p lines parallel to one side, and q lines parallel to the second side. Find the number of different rectangles in the resulting figure. Note that some of the rectangles may be contained in other rectangles.

CHAPTER 12

Mathematical Intuition

Just as the ability to compose great music is a gift that only a few are born with, so the ability to create great mathematics has been throughout the ages the possession of a mere handful.

Further the great mathematicians have almost universally demonstrated their genius at an early age. To cite just a few of the many examples: Gauss was reported to have found an error in his father's arithmetic before he was three years old and at nineteen he found the precise criterion for the constructibility of a regular polygon of n sides; Hamilton, Ireland's greatest mathematician, had mastered thirteen different languages by the age of fourteen, before he became interested in mathematics; Galois opened an entirely new branch of mathematics before he was killed in a duel at the age of twenty; and more recently the outstanding French mathematician Jacques Hadamard began publishing original work at the age of nineteen, and in 1896, at the age of thirty-one, published his proof of the prime number theorem, a theorem that had defied the efforts of all the leading mathematicians for the preceding one hundred years.

In the face of this evidence it would certainly seem to be pointless to try to teach anyone how to create new mathematics, and indeed our aim is more modest. Each person is born with a certain ability, and our objective is merely to provide the opportunity for the reader to develop his native ability to its maximum. It is true that "we never know what we can do until we try."

The rest of this chapter is devoted to stating certain mathematical propositions that may be either *true* or *false*. The reader should study the proposition carefully and try to decide for himself whether the assertion is true or false, and he should at least make a guess before consulting the answer in the back of the book. Most of these questions are difficult, and some are very difficult, and the reader is not expected to give a proof (or disproof) of the proposition. Of course if he should do so for a few of these problems that would be wonderful, and if he should give proofs (or disproofs) for the majority of them that would be fantastic. However, by examining these problems the reader will widen his mathematical horizon, and by guessing at the answers he should develop his mathematical intuition.

Example. We know from plane geometry that the perpendicular bisectors of the sides of a triangle meet at a point. Suppose that we modify this problem, by replacing the vertices of the triangle by three circles of arbitrary radii (Figure 12.1) and erecting the perpendicular bisectors of the three segments that lie outside the circles.

Assertion: These three perpendicular bisectors always meet in a point.

Is this proposition true or false?

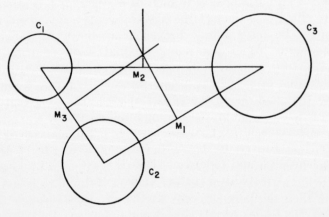

Fig. 12.1

This problem illustrates the process of generalization. If we regard the points as circles of zero radius then the original proposition about the perpendicular bisectors of a triangle, is a special case of this more general proposition. It would certainly be a pleasant surprise if the more general assertion turned out to be true.

We might try to settle this problem by making a few sketches similar to Figure 12.1, but with different triangles

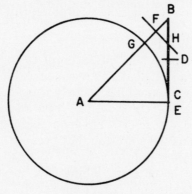

Fig. 12.2

and different radii for the circles. But since a drawing may be inaccurate, we could not accept the drawing itself either as a proof or a disproof. We might at last decide to try some special triangle that we know something about, and some special circles where not all the radii are zero. Eventually we might try the 45°-45°-90° triangle of Figure 12.2, where for simplicity we assume that the two equal sides each have unit length. Let us suppose further that the circle at A has radius 1, while the circles at B and C have radius 0, $i.e.$ they are points. If D, E, and F are the bisectors of the segments external to the circles, it is obvious that E coincides with C, and D lies on BC, $\frac{1}{2}$ unit away from either end point. The perpendicular at E will coincide with the segment BC, so that if the proposition is true then the perpendicular at F must pass through the point D. From the drawing it certainly does not seem to do this. To clinch the argument we compute as follows.

First $BG = \sqrt{2} - 1$ and hence $BF = (\sqrt{2} - 1)/2$. Since $\triangle BFH$ is a 45°-45°-90° triangle we find that

$$BH = \sqrt{\left(\frac{\sqrt{2}-1}{2}\right)^2 + \left(\frac{\sqrt{2}-1}{2}\right)^2}$$

$$= \sqrt{\frac{3-2\sqrt{2}}{4} + \frac{3-2\sqrt{2}}{4}} = \sqrt{\frac{3-2\sqrt{2}}{2}}.$$

But this is actually less than $BD = \frac{1}{2}$, just as the drawing shows. We leave the details of proving this inequality to the reader.

The assertion is false.

It may seem as though our attempt to create some new mathematics has failed and to a certain extent this is true. But we did prove something, namely that the conjecture is false, and consequently there has been an increase in our knowledge and our efforts have not been completely in vain. But it must be admitted that because of its negative nature our result is uninteresting.

This then is the pattern. Think of a question that can be treated logically and try to answer it. In just such a way is mathematics created. Try your hand at the following problems, or still better think up some of your own.

GEOMETRY

1. Let A, B, C be the vertices of an arbitrary triangle in the plane. It is always possible to find three circles with centers A, B, and C such that each circle is tangent to the other two, provided that the radii of the three circles are chosen properly.

2. In any convex quadrilateral, the two diagonals divide the quadrilateral into four triangles with areas A_1, A_2, A_3, and A_4, (see Figure 12.3). Assertion: For any convex quadrilateral

$$A_1 + A_3 = A_2 + A_4.$$

3. Under the conditions of problem 2

$$A_1 A_3 = A_2 A_4.$$

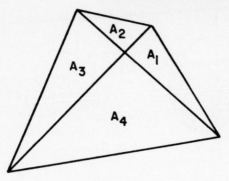

Fig. 12.3

4. For a circle every line that bisects the area also bisects the circumference. This is also true for any ellipse. But these are not all the curves with this property. Let C be any closed curve that has two axes of symmetry that are mutually perpendicular (see Figure 12.4). Then

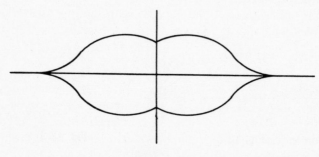

Fig. 12.4

every line that bisects the circumference of C also bisects the area enclosed by C.

5. A circle C_1 rolls inside a second circle C_2 without slipping (see Figure 12.5). If the radius of C_1 is one-half the radius of C_2, then a fixed point on C_1 will describe a straight line as C_1 rolls inside C_2.

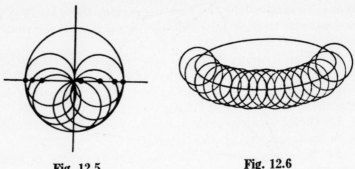

Fig. 12.5   **Fig. 12.6**

6. With each point on a given ellipse as center, a circle of fixed radius is drawn (Figure 12.6). All of these circles together form a region whose outer boundary is another ellipse.

7. Let *ABC* be an arbitrary triangle and suppose that the angle trisectors of the triangle meet pairwise in the points *P*, *Q*, and *R* as indicated in Figure 12.7. Then the triangle *PQR* is an equilateral triangle.

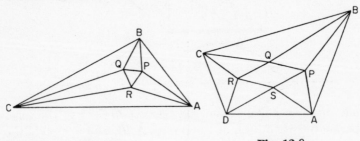

Fig. 12.7   **Fig. 12.8**

8. A generalization of problem 7. Let *ABCD* be an arbitrary convex quadrilateral and suppose that the angle trisectors of the quadrilateral meet pairwise in points *P*, *Q*, *R*, and *S* as indicated in Figure 12.8. Then the figure *PQRS* is a rhombus.

9. Six points in space are so placed that no three are on a line and no four lie in a plane. The fifteen lines joining the pairs of points in all possible ways are drawn and some of the lines are painted red and some are painted blue. No matter how the painting is done there is always at least one triangle in which all the sides have the same color.

10. Of all triangles inscribed in a circle, the one with the largest area is the equilateral triangle.

11. Of all triangles circumscribed about a fixed circle the one with the largest area is the equilateral triangle.

12. Of all quadrilaterals inscribed in a circle, the one with the largest area is the square.

13. Three skew edges of a cube (shown heavy in Figure 12.9) are selected and points A, B, and C are chosen,

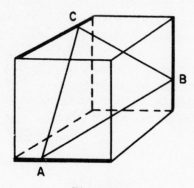

Fig. 12.9

one on each edge. Then the triangle ABC has the least perimeter when each of the points A, B, and C bisects the segment on which it lies.

14. Given three skew lines in space, points A, B, and C are chosen, one on each line. Then among all such triangles ABC the one with the least perimeter is an equilateral triangle.

15. Of all triangles with a given fixed area the triangle with the least perimeter is an equilateral triangle.

16. An equilateral triangle with each side of length 1 has perimeter $P = 3$ and area $A = \sqrt{3}/4$. Whence P and A satisfy the equation $P^2 = 12\sqrt{3}\,A$.

Assertion: For any triangle $P^2 \geqq 12\sqrt{3}\,A$.

17. The values $P = 3$, and $A = \sqrt{3}/4$ for the equilateral triangle of problem 16 also satisfy the equation $P = 4\sqrt{3}\, A$.

Assertion: For any triangle $P \geqq 4\sqrt{3}\, A$.

18. Given any convex region in the plane there is always some straight line that simultaneously bisects the area of the region and the length of the boundary curve.

19. Given two nonintersecting convex regions in the plane (Figure 12.10) there is always a straight line that simultaneously bisects the areas of both regions.

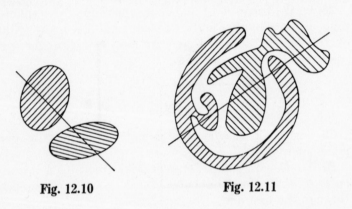

Fig. 12.10   **Fig. 12.11**

20. Suppose the word convex is omitted in problem 19 (see Figure 12.11). In this case the phrase "bisects the area" means that the area of that portion of the region lying on one side of the straight line is equal to the area of that portion of the region lying on the other side of the line. The region itself may be cut into many pieces by the line. There is always a straight line that simultaneously bisects both regions.

21. Given two nonintersecting regions in the plane there is always some straight line that bisects the first region and divides the second region in the ratio 2 to 1 (the area of the region on one side of the line is twice the area of the region on the other side of the line).

22. Suppose that the two regions in problem 21 are required to be convex.

23. Paul Erdös.[1] Given seven points in the plane, there are always three that do not form the vertices of an isosceles triangle. However it is possible to find six points in the plane such that any three do form the vertices of an isosceles triangle. (If A, B, and C lie on a line in that order we define ABC to be an isosceles triangle if and only if $AB = BC$.)

24. Paul Erdös. Let n points in the plane have the property that any line going through any two of them also passes through a third point of the set. Then all of the n points must lie on a single straight line.

25. C. W. Trigg. If A and B are the radii of two spheres tangent to each other and to a plane, and if R is the radius of the largest sphere that can pass between the two spheres and the plane, then

$$\frac{1}{\sqrt{R}} = \frac{1}{\sqrt{A}} + \frac{1}{\sqrt{B}}.$$

26. The main diagonals of a cube are mutually perpendicular.

27. H. D. Grossman. It is possible to cut a hole in a cube so that a second cube of the same size can pass through the first one.

ALGEBRA

A polynomial is an expression of the form

$$a_0 x^n + a_1 x^{n-1} + a_2 x^{n-2} + \cdots + a_{n-1} x + a_n$$

where a_0 is different from zero. The numbers a_0, a_1, a_2, $\cdots$, a_{n-1}, a_n are called the coefficients, and the polynomial is said to be of nth degree or of degree n. If $n = 1$ the polynomial is linear; if $n = 2$, it is quadratic; if $n = 3$,

---

[1] A number of these problems were first printed in the *American Mathematical Monthly*, and later reprinted in the *Otto Dunkel Memorial Problem Book*. We are grateful to the Mathematical Association of America for their kind permission to reproduce these problems. Such problems are indicated by giving the name of the composer.

it is cubic; etc. If we can find a value for x such that the equation

$$a_0 x^n + a_1 x^{n-1} + a_2 x^{n-2} + \cdots + a_{n-1} + a_n = 0$$

is satisfied, x is called a root (or zero) of the polynomial. For example the polynomial

$$x^3 - 2x^2 - 5x + 6$$

is a cubic polynomial with coefficients $1, -2, -5$, and 6, and it has as roots the numbers $x = 1, 3$, and -2. A polynomial may have complex roots, for example $x^2 + ix + i - 1$ has the roots $x = -1$ and $x = 1 - i$, where i denotes as usual $\sqrt{-1}$.

1. Every polynomial with all coefficients real has a real root.

2. Every polynomial of degree greater than or equal to 1 has at least one root, real or complex.

3. A polynomial of nth degree $(n \geqq 1)$ always has n different roots.

4. A polynomial of nth degree $(n \geqq 1)$ cannot have more than n different roots.

5. Every polynomial with all coefficients real, and of odd degree has at least one real root.

6. Let $x = 7 + \sqrt{5}$ be the root of a polynomial in which all of the coefficients are integers. Then $x = 7 - \sqrt{5}$ is also a root of the same polynomial.

7. The number $x = \sqrt{2} + \sqrt{3}$ is a root of some second degree polynomial with all the coefficients integers.

8. The assertion of problem 7 except that the polynomial is of third degree.

9. The assertion of problem 7 except that the polynomial is of fourth degree.

10. If a polynomial $a_0 x^n + a_1 x^{n-1} + \cdots + a_n$ is known to have n distinct roots $r_1, r_2, \cdots, r_n$ then the polynomial can be factored thus

$$a_0 x^n + a_1 x^{n-1} + \cdots + a_n = a_0 (x - r_1)(x - r_2) \cdots (x - r_n).$$

11. When the nth order determinant

$$D = \begin{vmatrix} 1 & 1 & 1 & 1 & \cdots & 1 \\ 1 & x-1 & 1 & 1 & \cdots & 1 \\ 1 & 1 & x-2 & 1 & \cdots & 1 \\ 1 & 1 & 1 & x-3 & \cdots & 1 \\ \cdot & \cdot & \cdot & \cdot & \cdots & \cdot \\ 1 & 1 & 1 & 1 & \cdots & x-(n-1) \end{vmatrix}$$

is expanded it is obviously a polynomial in x of degree $n-1$. Find all of the roots of this polynomial and express D as a product as indicated in problem 10.

12. It is possible to find some values for x, y, z, and w so that the determinant

$$\begin{vmatrix} x^2 & (x+1)^2 & (x+2)^2 & (x+3)^2 \\ y^2 & (y+1)^2 & (y+2)^2 & (y+3)^2 \\ z^2 & (z+1)^2 & (z+2)^2 & (z+3)^2 \\ w^2 & (w+1)^2 & (w+2)^2 & (w+3)^2 \end{vmatrix}$$

is not zero.

13. The polynomial $x^4 - x^3 - 6x^2 + 5x - 1$ can be factored. Indeed it is easy to check by multiplication of the two terms on the right that

$$x^4 - x^3 - 6x^2 + 5x - 1 = (\tfrac{2}{3}x^2 - 2x + \tfrac{2}{3})(\tfrac{3}{2}x^2 + 3x - \tfrac{3}{2}).$$

Notice that the coefficients in the factors are all rational numbers (fractions). But we can convert them all to integers by multiplying the first factor by $\tfrac{3}{2}$ and multiplying the second factor by its reciprocal $\tfrac{2}{3}$. Then we find that

$$x^4 - x^3 - 6x^2 + 5x - 1 = (x^2 - 3x + 1)(x^2 + 2x - 1).$$

This example illustrates the following assertion.

If a polynomial with integer coefficients can be factored into the product of two polynomials with rational coefficients, then it can be factored into the product of two polynomials with integer coefficients.

14. If a polynomial has integer coefficients and if the value of the polynomial is an odd integer both when $x = 0$ and when $x = 1$, then the polynomial can not have an integer root.

15. For each positive integer n

(a)
$$\left(1+\frac{1}{n}\right)^n < \left(1+\frac{1}{n+1}\right)^{n+1}$$

and

(b)
$$\left(1+\frac{1}{n}\right)^n < 3.$$

SEQUENCES AND SERIES

A *sequence* is a set of numbers in which there is a first one, and a second one, and a third one, etc. The numbers of a sequence may be denoted in some such fashion as

$$s_1, s_2, s_3, \cdots s_n, \cdots$$

in which s_1 is the first number, s_2 is the second number and so on, so that the subscript denotes the place of the number in the sequence.

For example the numbers

$$\frac{1}{2}, \frac{3}{4}, \frac{7}{8}, \frac{15}{16}, \cdots, \frac{2^n-1}{2^n}, \cdots$$

form a sequence, where the notation clearly shows that the nth term of the sequence is $(2^n-1)/2^n$. In this particular case it is obvious that the terms of the sequence become closer and closer to 1 as n increases indefinitely. In this case we say that *1 is the limit of the sequence as n tends to infinity*. We also say that *the sequence converges to 1*. Not every sequence is convergent, for example the sequence

$$-1, +1, -1, +1, \cdots, (-1)^n \cdots$$

is not convergent because it does not get closer and closer to any single number but oscillates between -1 and $+1$. In such a case we say that *the sequence diverges*.

In each of problems 1 through 5 state whether the sequence converges or diverges, and if the sequence converges give the limit.

1. $1, \dfrac{1}{2}, \dfrac{1}{3}, \dfrac{1}{4}, \cdots, \dfrac{1}{n}, \cdots$.

2. $1, 4, 9, 16, \cdots, n^2, \cdots$.

3. $8, 1, \dfrac{8}{27}, \dfrac{1}{8}, \cdots, \dfrac{8}{n^3}, \cdots$.

4. $3, \dfrac{7}{5}, \dfrac{4}{5}, \cdots, \dfrac{n+5}{n^2+1}, \cdots$.

5. $4, \dfrac{10}{3}, 3, \dfrac{14}{5}, \cdots, \dfrac{2n+6}{n+1}, \cdots$.

★6. $2, \dfrac{9}{4}, \dfrac{64}{27}, \dfrac{625}{256}, \cdots, \left(1+\dfrac{1}{n}\right)^n, \cdots$.

The nth term of a sequence need not be given directly but can be given indirectly in a variety of ways. The simplest such example is one in which the nth term is the sum of the first n terms of an infinite series. For example the series

$$(1) \qquad 1 + \frac{1}{2} + \frac{1}{4} + \frac{1}{8} + \cdots + \frac{1}{2^{n-1}} + \cdots$$

is supposed to have infinitely many terms, and the general law of formation of the nth term is clearly indicated by the term $1/2^{n-1}$. Then the sequence that we wish to examine is the one in which s_n is the sum of the first n terms. In this case we find that:

$s_1 = 1 \qquad\qquad = 1, \quad s_4 = 1 + \frac{1}{2} + \frac{1}{4} + \frac{1}{8} \qquad\qquad\;\; = \frac{15}{8},$

$s_2 = 1 + \frac{1}{2} \qquad\; = \frac{3}{2}, \quad s_5 = 1 + \frac{1}{2} + \frac{1}{4} + \frac{1}{8} + \frac{1}{16} \qquad = \frac{31}{16},$

$s_3 = 1 + \frac{1}{2} + \frac{1}{4} = \frac{7}{4}, \quad s_6 = 1 + \frac{1}{2} + \frac{1}{4} + \frac{1}{8} + \frac{1}{16} + \frac{1}{32} = \frac{63}{32}.$

It is intuitively obvious that as n increases (as more and more terms are added) s_n approaches 2. In such a case we say that the series (1) is *convergent* and that its *sum* is 2. If the sequence s_n does not have a limit the series is said to be *divergent*.

In problems 7 through 12 state whether the series diverges or converges and if the series converges give the sum of the series.

7. $1 - 1 + 1 - 1 + \cdots + (-1)^{n+1} + \cdots$.

8. $1 + \dfrac{1}{3} + \dfrac{1}{9} + \dfrac{1}{27} + \cdots + \dfrac{1}{3^{n-1}} + \cdots$.

9. $1 + 2 + 3 + 4 + \cdots + n + \cdots$.

10. $1 + \dfrac{1}{1 \cdot 2} + \dfrac{1}{2 \cdot 3} + \dfrac{1}{3 \cdot 4} + \dfrac{1}{4 \cdot 5} + \cdots + \dfrac{1}{n(n+1)} + \cdots$.

11. $1 + \dfrac{1}{2} + \dfrac{1}{3} + \dfrac{1}{4} + \dfrac{1}{5} + \cdots + \dfrac{1}{n} + \cdots$.

12. $1 + \dfrac{1}{10} + \dfrac{1}{100} + \dfrac{1}{1000} + \cdots + \dfrac{1}{10^{n-1}} + \cdots$.

★13. If we compute in the series

$$8\left(\frac{1}{1 \cdot 3} + \frac{1}{5 \cdot 7} + \frac{1}{9 \cdot 11} + \cdots + \frac{1}{(4n-3)(4n-1)} + \cdots\right)$$

with 5-figure accuracy we find that

$s_1 = 2.6667$	$s_4 = 3.0170$
$s_2 = 2.8952$	$s_5 = 3.0418$
$s_3 = 2.9760$	$s_6 = 3.0584.$

The assertion is that in the limit as n increases, s_n approaches π, so that the sum of this infinite series is π.

14. $\dfrac{\pi}{4} = 1 - \dfrac{1}{3} + \dfrac{1}{5} - \dfrac{1}{7} + \dfrac{1}{9} - \cdots + \dfrac{(-1)^{n+1}}{2n+1} + \cdots$.

★15. In this sequence the nth term is given by the complicated looking fraction

$$s_n = \cfrac{1}{2 + \cfrac{1}{2 + \cfrac{1}{2 + \cfrac{1}{2 + \cfrac{1}{\ddots}}}}}$$

$$+ \frac{1}{2}$$

in which there are n twos and n ones. Direct computation gives:

$$s_1 = \tfrac{1}{2}, \quad s_2 = \tfrac{2}{5}, \quad s_3 = \tfrac{5}{12}, \quad \cdots.$$

In general we can find s_n from the preceding term s_{n-1} by the formula

$$s_n = \frac{1}{2 + s_{n-1}}.$$

For example

$$s_4 = \frac{1}{2 + s_3} = \frac{1}{2 + \frac{5}{12}} = \frac{12}{24 + 5} = \frac{12}{29} = .41379 \cdots.$$

The assertion is that the limit of this sequence is $\sqrt{2} - 1 = .414214 \cdots$.

THE FIBONACCI SEQUENCE

About 1200 A.D. Fibonacci first studied a remarkable sequence of numbers, now known by his name. The nth Fibonacci number is denoted by u_n and the first two numbers of the sequence are $u_1 = 1$ and $u_2 = 1$. Thereafter each number of the sequence is obtained by adding the two preceding numbers. Thus by the definition of the Fibonacci sequence

(2) $$u_{n+1} = u_n + u_{n-1}.$$

Direct computation gives for the first ten numbers of this sequence:

$$1, 1, 2, 3, 5, 8, 13, 21, 34, 55.$$

The assertions in problems 1 through 10 can all be proved using equation (2) and mathematical induction. In each problem n is any positive integer.

1. $u_1 + u_2 + u_3 + \cdots + u_n = u_{n+2} - 1$.

2. $u_1 + u_3 + u_5 + \cdots + u_{2n-1} = u_{2n}$.

3. $1 + u_2 + u_4 + u_6 + \cdots + u_{2n} = u_{2n+1}$.

4. $\begin{vmatrix} u_n & u_{n+1} \\ u_{n+1} & u_{n+2} \end{vmatrix} = (-1)^{n+1}$.

5. $u_1^2 + u_2^2 + u_3^2 + \cdots + u_n^2 = u_n u_{n+1}$.

6. $u_1 - u_2 + u_3 - u_4 + \cdots (-1)^n u_{n+1} = 1 + (-1)^n u_n.$

★**7.** $u_n = \dfrac{1}{\sqrt{5}} \left\{ \left(\dfrac{1 + \sqrt{5}}{2} \right)^n - \left(\dfrac{1 - \sqrt{5}}{2} \right)^n \right\}.$

★**8.** $u_1 u_2 + u_2 u_3 + u_3 u_4 + \cdots + u_{2n-1} u_{2n} = u_{2n}{}^2.$

★**9.** $u_1 u_2 + u_2 u_3 + u_3 u_4 + \cdots + u_{2n} u_{2n+1} = u_{2n+1}{}^2 - 1.$

★**10.** $u_{n+5} = 5 u_{n+1} + 3 u_n.$

NUMBER THEORY

1. Observe that as we let $n = 1, 2, 3, \cdots$ in the expression $8n + 1$ we get a sequence of numbers that seems to include all of the squares of the odd numbers. For example computation gives:

$$\begin{aligned}
&\text{If } n = 1, \text{ then } 8n + 1 = 9 = 3^2, \\
&\text{If } n = 2, \text{ then } 8n + 1 = 17, \\
&\text{If } n = 3, \text{ then } 8n + 1 = 25 = 5^2, \\
&\text{If } n = 4, \text{ then } 8n + 1 = 33, \\
&\text{If } n = 5, \text{ then } 8n + 1 = 41, \\
&\text{If } n = 6, \text{ then } 8n + 1 = 49 = 7^2, \\
&\text{If } n = 10, \text{ then } 8n + 1 = 81 = 9^2, \\
&\text{If } n = 15, \text{ then } 8n + 1 = 121 = 11^2, \\
&\text{If } n = 21, \text{ then } 8n + 1 = 169 = 13^2, \\
&\text{If } n = 28, \text{ then } 8n + 1 = 225 = 15^2.
\end{aligned}$$

The assertion is that as n runs through the integers $1, 2, 3, \cdots$ the sequence of numbers $s_n = 8n + 1$ includes the squares of all the odd integers.

2. In contrast to problem 1, the expression $10n + 3$ is never the square of an integer for any integer value of n.

3. The expression $10n + 3$ is never the cube of an integer for any integer value of n.

4. Any integer of the form $4k + 1$ is the sum of the squares of two integers. For example:

$$\begin{aligned}
&\text{If } k = 1, \quad \text{then } 4k + 1 = 5 = 1^2 + 2^2, \\
&\text{If } k = 2, \quad \text{then } 4k + 1 = 9 = 0^2 + 3^2, \\
&\text{If } k = 3, \quad \text{then } 4k + 1 = 13 = 2^2 + 3^2, \\
&\text{If } k = 13, \text{ then } 4k + 1 = 53 = 2^2 + 7^2.
\end{aligned}$$

5. Any integer of the form $4k + 3$ is never the sum of the squares of two integers.

6. Any prime number of the form $4k + 1$ is the sum of the squares of two integers.

7. For all values of a, b, c, and d

$$(a^2 + b^2)(c^2 + d^2) = (ac - bd)^2 + (ad + bc)^2.$$

8. If X is the sum of the squares of two integers and if Y is the sum of the squares of two integers, then their product XY is the sum of the squares of two integers.

9. A number n is called a *perfect number* if the sum of its divisors is equal to $2n$. For example 6 and 28 are perfect numbers. A number n is said to be *abundant* if the sum of all of its divisors is greater than $2n$, and it is called *deficient* if the sum of all of its divisors is less than $2n$. For example the number 80 is abundant. To see this we write 80 in the factored form $80 = 2^4 \cdot 5$ and then it is easy to list all of its divisors. We find

$$1 + 2 + 4 + 5 + 8 + 10 + 16 + 20 + 40 + 80 = 186$$

and this is greater than $2 \times 80 = 160$.

The assertion is that there are no odd abundant numbers.

10. There is an integer N such that $N/2$ is a perfect square (the square of an integer) and $N/3$ is a perfect cube.

11. The product of any four consecutive integers is always one less than a perfect square.

★12. W. C. Rufus. There is an integer M such that $M/2$ is a perfect square, $M/3$ is a perfect cube, and $M/5$ is a perfect fifth power.

★13. Paul Erdös. Given $n + 1$ positive integers each less than or equal to $2n$, there is always at least one integer from the set that is divisible by some other integer from the set.

14. R. K. Morley. The improper cancellation

$$\frac{26}{65} = \frac{2\cancel{6}}{\cancel{6}5} = \frac{2}{5}$$

gives a correct result and in lowest terms. There are four other proper fractions with denominators less than a hundred that can be reduced to lowest terms by the same type of wrong cancellation.

★15. W. R. Ransom. If we compute $(\sqrt{2}-1)^n$ for various positive integer values of n we find:

$$(\sqrt{2}-1)^1 \qquad\qquad\qquad = \sqrt{2}-\sqrt{1},$$
$$(\sqrt{2}-1)^2 = 2-2\sqrt{2}+1 \qquad\qquad = \sqrt{9}-\sqrt{8},$$
$$(\sqrt{2}-1)^3 = 2\sqrt{2}-3\cdot 2+3\sqrt{2}-1 \qquad = \sqrt{50}-\sqrt{49}.$$
$$(\sqrt{2}-1)^4 = 4-4\cdot 2\sqrt{2}+6\cdot 2-4\sqrt{2}+1 = \sqrt{289}-\sqrt{288}$$

The assertion is that for every positive integer n

$$(\sqrt{2}-1)^n = \sqrt{A+1}-\sqrt{A}$$

for an appropriate integer A.

ANSWERS TO PROBLEMS

Chapter 1. Exer. 1 Page 22

1. $\dfrac{\dfrac{A}{B}}{\dfrac{C}{D}} = \dfrac{AD}{BC}$, $\dfrac{\dfrac{A}{B}}{D} = \dfrac{A}{BCD}$,

$\dfrac{A}{\dfrac{B}{\dfrac{C}{D}}} = \dfrac{ACD}{B}$, $\dfrac{A}{\dfrac{B}{\dfrac{C}{D}}} = \dfrac{AC}{BD}$

$\dfrac{\dfrac{A}{B}}{\dfrac{C}{D}} = \dfrac{AC}{BD}$. **2.** $\dfrac{A}{BC} = \dfrac{AC}{B}$ if and only if $C = \pm 1$.

3. $f(1) = 1-2+3-4 = -2$, $f(2) = 8-8+6-4 = 2$, etc. **4.** $f(5) = 2^5 = 32$. **5.** $f(x+y) = 11(x+y) = 11x+11y = f(x)+f(y)$. **6.** $x^2 = (-x)^2$, $(x+6)^2 = x^2+12x+36$. **7.** $(-x)^7 = -x^7$, $(xy)^7 = x^7 y^7$. **8.** $5^{x+y} = 5^x 5^y$. **9.** (a) $7+9+11+13+15$ (b) $16+25+36$ (c) $-32+64-128$. **10.** $250 \times 501 = 125{,}250$. **11.** $200 \times 401 - 10 = 80{,}190$. **12.** $250{,}500$. **13.** $500 \times 1001 - 250{,}500 = 250{,}000$. **14.** (a) $4-\sqrt{15}$ (b) $\sqrt{5}-\sqrt[3]{11}$ (c) $x^2-2xy+y^2$ since it is $(x-y)^2$ and this is always positive or zero.

Chapter 2. Exer. 1 Page 30

15. $n = 1$, or $n \geqq 5$.   **16.** $n = 1$, or $n \geqq 10$.

Chapter 2. Exer. 2 Page 33

1. $n = 1$.   **2.** No.   **3.** $m = 1, n = 1$.   **4.** $n = 8$.

Chapter 2. Exer. 3 Page 36

1. 1, 8, 28, 56, 70, 56, 28, 8, 1; 1, 9, 36, 84, 126, 126, 84, 36, 9, 1.   **2.** 1080.   **3.** $-\frac{7}{324}$.   **4.** $(2n + 1)^2 - 1 = 4n^2 + 4n = 4n(n + 1)$ and one of the last two factors must be even.   **5.** The same as problem 4. **6.** $(3n - 1)^3 + 1 = 9n[3n(n - 1) + 1]$ and the quantity in square brackets is always odd because $n(n - 1)$ is always even.   **7.** $(n - 1)^3 + n^3 + (n + 1)^3 = 3n(n^2 + 2)$.   **8.** In the expansion of $(x + y)^{n-1}$ put $x = 1$ and $y = 1$. The left side is $(1 + 1)^{n-1} = 2^{n-1}$ and the right side is the sum of the numbers in the nth row of Pascal's triangle.

Chapter 2. Exer. 4 Page 39

1. Since $(x + y)^n = (y + x)^n$ the coefficient of $x^{n-k} y^k$ on the left must equal the coefficient of $y^k x^{n-k}$ on the right. **2.** 1001.   **3.** $- 2002$.   **4.** Put $x = 1$, and $y = 1$ in equation (13).   **5.** Put $x = 1$, $y = - 1$ in equation (13) (see problem 8 of exer. 3).

Chapter 3. Exer. 1 Page 45

1. $1 + 2 \neq 1 + 3 \neq 1 + 4$.   **2.** If there were such a magic square we could subtract the smallest element in the square from each element, divide by the common difference, if it is not zero, and then add 1 to each element. This would give a magic square with the elements 1, 2, 3, 4. But this is impossible.

3.

8	1	6		4	3	8		4	9	2
3	5	7		9	5	1		3	5	7
4	9	2		2	7	6		8	1	6

6	1	8		2	7	6
7	5	3		9	5	1
2	9	4		4	3	8

4. $1 + 2 + 3 + \ldots + 16 = 4S.$ **5.** 65.   **6.** $1 + 2 + 3 +$ $\ldots + n^2 = nS.$

Chapter 3. Exer. 2 Page 48
1. (a) $t = 5,$ $a = 1,$ $b = -3,$ (b) $t = 8,$ $a = 1,$ $b = -3,$ (c) $t = 16,$ $a = 2,$ $b = -6,$ (d) $t = 5,$ $a = -3,$ $b = -1,$ (e) $t = 5,$ $a = 3,$ $b = -1.$
5. Yes.

6.

16	3	2	13
5	10	11	8
9	6	7	12
4	15	14	1

7. $W = 15,$ $X = 2,$ $Y = 8,$ $Z = 9,$ $A = -12,$ $B = -4,$ $C = 4,$ $D = -8.$ **9.** $W = 5,$ $X = 3,$ $Y = 10,$ $Z = 16,$ $A = -4,$ $B = 1,$ $C = 4,$ $D = -5.$

Chapter 3. Exer. 3 Page 56
1. $1 + 2 + \ldots + n^3 = n^2 S.$ **5.** $3 \times 16 = 48.$ **6.** 16.
7. $16 \times 13 = 208.$ **8.** $16 \times 9 + 16 \times 15 = 384.$
9. $16 \times 15 = 240.$

Chapter 4. Exer. 1 Page 64
1. $(a - 1)^2 \geqq 0.$ **2.** $(2a - 5b)^2 \geqq 0.$ **3.** $(\sqrt{c} - \sqrt{d})^2 \geqq 0.$
4. $(c - d)^2 + 4cd \geqq 4cd.$ **5.** $(\sqrt{a/b} - \sqrt{b/a})^2 \geqq 0,$
$(\sqrt{a} - \sqrt{b})^2 \geqq 0.$ **6.** $(a - b)^2 \geqq 0.$
7. $(x - 2y)^2 \geqq 0.$ **8.** $(x - y)^2 + (y - z)^2 + (z - x)^2 \geqq 0.$
9. $(c - d)^4 \geqq 0.$ **10.** $(a - 3b)^2 \geqq 0.$ **11.** $(c - d)^2$
$(c + d) \geqq 0.$ **12.** $A/D + D/A \geqq 2$ and $B/C + C/B \geqq 2.$
13. 4, 6, 7, 8, 9.   **14.** $\sqrt{19} + \sqrt{21}.$
15. $\sqrt{11} - \sqrt{8}.$ **16.** $5\sqrt{7}.$ **17.** $\sqrt[3]{23}.$ **20.** $x < -2.$
21. $x > \frac{1}{3}.$ **22.** $x > 1$ or $x < 0.$ **23.** $1 < x < 8.$
24. $3 < x < 5.$ **25.** $\frac{1}{4} < x < 3.$

Chapter 4. Exer. 2 Page 69
1. Use math. ind. Mult. both sides by ab and add on the right side the positive quantity $(a^{2n+1} - b^{2n+1})(a - b).$
2. Use math. ind. First prove that $\dfrac{1}{\sqrt{n+1}} > \sqrt{n+1} - \sqrt{n}.$

3. $w_k a_1 < w_k a_k < w_k a_n$ for each k. Add n such inequalities and divide through by $w_1 + w_2 + \ldots + w_n$.　　**4.** Use b_k as w_k on the numbers a_k/b_k in problem 3. In problems **5, 6, 7,** and **8** use theorem 10.　　**9.** Use math. ind. First prove that $(1 - a_{n+1})(1 + a_1 + a_2 + \ldots + a_{n+1}) < 1 + a_1 + a_2 + \ldots + a_n$.　　**10.** By the hint, $2(abcd + 1) \geqq (ab + 1)(cd + 1)$, and use the hint two more times. **11.** First prove that $\frac{1}{2}(a + b) \leqq \frac{a^2 + b^2}{a + b}$ and then add three such terms.　　**12.** Expand the left side and use the hint.　　**13.** Use theorem 10 on the six terms on the right side.　　**14.** Use math. ind. Prove that

$$\frac{4(n + 1)}{n + 2} \leqq \frac{(2n + 1)(2n + 2)}{(n + 1)^2}.$$

Chapter 5. Exer. 1 Page 75

1. When a new point is added on a line, it divides a previous segment (or ray) into two pieces, so one new piece is added. Hence $F(k + 1) = F(k) + 1$.　　**2.** $F(k + 1) = F(k) + 2k$.　　**3.** Combine the methods of examples 1 and 2.　　**4.** Set $k = 2$.　　**5.** Prove that $F(k + 1) = F(k) + 2k$ and then add.　　**6.** From example 2 we have $F(k + 1) = F(k) + \frac{1}{2}(k^2 + k + 2)$. Then add $n - 1$ such terms and use the formula $1^2 + 2^2 + 3^2 + \ldots + (n - 1)^2 = \frac{1}{6}(n - 1)n(2n - 1)$ which is another form of the formula proved in problem 4 of exer. 1 in Chapter 2.　　**7.** Regard the $(k + 1)$th sphere that is added as a plane. Then by problem 5 this sphere is divided into $k^2 - k + 2$ parts by the other k spheres, and these parts form the boundaries of $k^2 - k + 2$ new regions. Then $F(k + 1) = F(k) + k^2 - k + 2$. Adding $n - 1$ such equations gives $F(n) = \frac{1}{3}n(n^2 - 3n + 8)$.

Chapter 5. Exer. 2 Page 79

3. Let $F(k)$ be the number of diagonals in a polygon of k sides. The introduction of a new vertex gives the possibility of drawing $k - 1$ new diagonals. Then $F(k + 1) = F(k) + k - 1$. Add the equations formed for $k = 3, 4, 5, \ldots, n - 1$. An easier method of solution will be covered in Chapter 11.　　**4.** Figure A shows the case when $n = 6$.

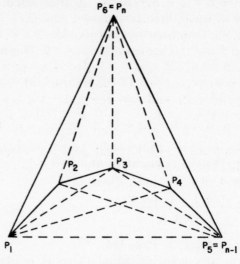

Fig. A

The diagonals are dotted. In general we place $n-3$ vertices inside the triangle $P_1P_{n-1}P_n$. Hence exactly $n-3$ diagonals lie inside the polygon. By problem 3 there are $n(n-3)/2$ diagonals altogether. Hence there must be $n(n-3)/2 - (n-3) = (n-2)(n-3)/2$ diagonals outside. **5.** By problem 3 the total number of diagonals is $n(n-3)/2$. By problems 1 and 2 there is always at least $n-3$ diagonals inside the polygonal. Hence the largest possible number of diagonals outside the polygon is $n(n-3)/2 - (n-3)$. But this is $(n-2)(n-3)/2$.

Chapter 5. Exer. 3 Page 83

1. $12 - 18 + 8 = 2$. **2.** $(n+3) - (2n+3) + (n+2) = 2$. **3.** $(n+1) - 2n + (n+1) = 2$. **4.** $V = (p+2)(q+2)$, $E = (p+1)(q+2) + (q+1)(p+2)$, $F = (p+1)(q+1) + 1$. **5.** $V = pq + 1$, $E = 2pq$, $F = pq + 1$. **6.** No.

Chapter 5. Exer. 4 Page 87

1. If there were such a map, then $V = 5$, $E = 10$, and

$F = 2 - V + E = 2 - 5 + 10 = 7$.   But   each   country
must have at least three boundaries, and each boundary
serves exactly two countries, hence $3F \leqq 2 \times 10$. Thus
$F \leqq 6$, and $F = 7$. This is impossible.   **2.** Since $3V = 2E$,   then   3 divides E.   **4.** (a) $4 - 6 + 4 = 2$,
(b) $8 - 12 + 6 = 2$, (c) $6 - 12 + 8 = 2$, (d) $20 - 30 + 12 = 2$,   (e) $12 - 30 + 20 = 2$.   **5.** $n + 1 - 2n + n + 1 = 2$.
6. $2n - 3n + n + 2 = 2$.   **9.** If $E = 7$ then from problem 8 we find $\frac{13}{3} \leqq V \leqq \frac{14}{3}$. But the number of vertices
must be an integer. Since there is no integer between
$4\frac{1}{3}$ and $4\frac{2}{3}$, this is impossible, and hence no such polyhedron exists.

Chapter 7. Exer. 1 Page 110
3 2.   **4.** 3, 5.   **5.** 6.

Chapter 7. Exer. 3 Page 114
1. The two foci coincide at the center of the circle.
3. Draw the angle bisector at the point of intersection of
the lines l and p.

Chapter 8. Exer. 1 Page 120
1. Yes, the line of problem 2.

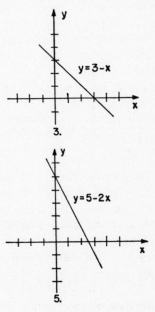

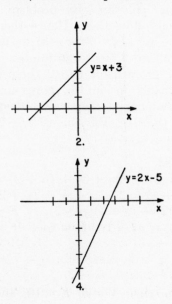

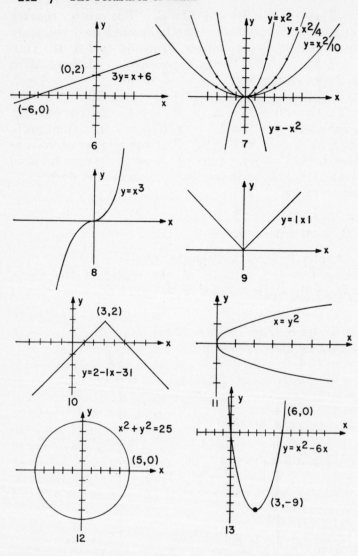

Chapter 8. Exer. 2 Page 125

1. Minimum $y = 3$ at $x = 2$. **2.** Maximum $y = 10$ at $x = 6$. **3.** Maximum $y = -5$ at $x = -4$. **4.** Minimum $y = -14$ at $x = -1$. **5.** Maximum $y = 5$ at $x = 1$. **6.** Minimum $y = -2$ at $x = -2$. **7.** No maximum or minimum. **8.** No maximum or minimum.

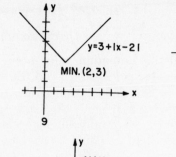

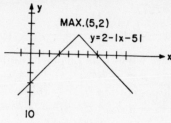

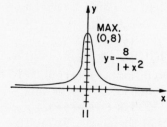

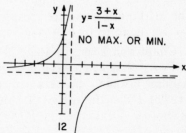

Chapter 8. Exer. 3 Page 129

1. $y = 1 + x^2(3 - x)$,   rel. min. $y = 1$ at $x = 0$;
$y = 5 - (x - 2)^2(x + 1)$,   rel. max. $y = 5$ at $x = 2$.
2. $y = 11 - (x - 1)^2(7 - x)$,   rel. max. $y = 11$ at $x = 1$;
$y = -21 + (x - 5)^2(x + 1)$,   rel. min. $y = -21$ at $x = 5$.
3. $y = -37 + (x + 2)^2(11 - 2x)$,   rel. min. $y = -37$ at
$x = -2$; $y = 88 - (x - 3)^2(2x + 9)$,   rel. max. $y = 88$ at
$x = 3$.   **4.** $y = 69 - (x + 4)^2(5 - x)$, rel. max. $y = 69$ at
$x = -4$; $y = -39 + (x - 2)^2(x + 7)$, rel. min. $y = -39$
at $x = 2$.   **5.** $y = 1 + x^2(8 - x^2)$, rel. min. $y = 1$ at $x = 0$;
$y = 17 - (x + 2)^2(x - 2)^2$, rel. max. $y = 17$ at $x = -2$ or
$x = 2$.   **6.** $y = 20 - (x - 1)^2(7 + 2x - x^2)$, rel. max.
$y = 20$ at $x = 1$; $y = 4 + (x + 1)^2(x - 3)^2$, rel. min. $y = 4$
at $x = -1$ or $x = 3$.

Chapter 8. Exer. 4 Page 132

1. 10, 10.   **2.** 19, 19.   **3.** $s/2$, $s/2$, the max. of the
product is $s^2/4$.   **5.** $2r^2$.   **6.** Max. area is 15 when
$y = 3$.   **7.** $bh/4$.

Chapter 8. Exer. 5 Page 137

1. $16 \times 16 \times 4 = 1024$ cu. in.   **2.** $\left(2\dfrac{L}{3}\right)\left(2\dfrac{L}{3}\right)\left(\dfrac{L}{6}\right) =$

214 / The Pleasures of Math

$2L^3/27$.   **4.** Since $ax^2 + bx + c = a\left(x + \dfrac{b}{2a}\right)^2 + \dfrac{4ac - b^2}{4a}$,   then $\dfrac{4ac - b^2}{4a}$ is the minimum value when a is positive, and this minimum value occurs when $x = -b/2a$.   **5.** Use $(4ac - b^2)/4a$.   **6.** Both sides give $(a_1b_2)^2 + (b_1a_2)^2 - 2a_1a_2b_1b_2$. Consequently $(a_1b_1 + a_2b_2)^2 \leqq (a_1{}^2 + a_2{}^2)(b_1{}^2 + b_2{}^2)$.   **7.** Set $b_1 = b_2 = b_3 = \cdots = b_n = 1$ in (16).   **8.** Apply the fact that the arithmetic mean is greater than or equal to the geometric mean to $(a_1b_1 + a_2b_2 + \cdots + a_nb_n)/n$.

Chapter 9. Exer. 1. Page 142
1. Prove that $\triangle P_1AP_2 \cong \triangle P_1BP_2$.   **2.** Yes.   **3.** A regular hexagon has six concurrent axes of symmetry. **11.** Let P' be the image of P in l and let Q' be the image of Q in m. Draw the line $P'Q'$.   **12.** Let C' and C'' be the image points of C in the two sides of the angle. Draw the line $C'C''$.

Chapter 9. Exer. 2. Page 150
1. $d = 5\sqrt{34}$ ft on path III of Figure 9.9.   **2.** $d = 30$ ft on path I of Figure 9.9.   **3.** Use $d_3 = \sqrt{(w + l)^2 + (y - x)^2}$ and $d_1 = x + l + y$ and set $d_3{}^2 < d_1{}^2$.   **4.** Use $d_2 = \sqrt{\left(x + l + \dfrac{w}{2}\right)^2 + \left(\dfrac{w}{2} + y\right)^2}$ and set $d_2{}^2 < d_1{}^2$.   **5.** Set $d_2{}^2 < d_3{}^2$.   **6.** Over the edge BV $d = 5\sqrt{3} - 1 \approx 7.65$, across the back face $\triangle AVC$ $d = 5 + \sqrt{3} \approx 6.73$ is the shortest path. (NOTE: $\approx$ means approximately.)   **9.** With A as center draw a circle of radius r. If P is on this circle $BP + CP$ is a minimum if and only if $\angle APB = \angle APC$. If the angle at A is equal to or greater than 120° the minimum occurs when P is at A.

Chapter 9. Exer. 3 Page 159
2. (a) No. A line parallel to the base of an equilateral triangle of unit side, and $\sqrt{6}/4$ units from the vertex, will bisect the area, but the perimeter falls into two parts of lengths $\sqrt{2}$ and $3 - \sqrt{2}$. (b) No. (c) Yes.   **3.** The area does not change, but the perimeter decreases.   **4.** The area of a circle with perimeter L is $L^2/4\pi$.   **6.** $V \leqq E^3/1728$.

Chapter 10. Exer. 1 Page 163
1. If $a = q_1 d$ and $b = q_2 d$ then $a + b = (q_1 + q_2)d$ and $a - b = (q_1 - q_2)d$. **2.** If d divides a and d divides $a + b$ then d must divide $(a + b) - a = b$. But by hypothesis d does not divide b. This is a contradiction so d does not divide $a + b$. **3.** If $a = qd$ then $-a = (-q)d$ so d divides $-a$. **4.** If $d_1 > \sqrt{a}$ and $d_2 > \sqrt{a}$ then $d_1 d_2 > a$. So if $d_1 d_2 = a$ at least one $d \leq \sqrt{a}$. **5.** 101, 103, 107, 109, 113, 127, 131, 137, 139, 149, 151, 157, 163, 167, 173, 179, 181, 191, 193, 197, 199. **6.** No. $f(41)$ is divisible by 41. **7.** (a) 7, 11, 13. (b) 73, 137. (c) 3, 7, 11, 13, 37. **8.** 7, 11. **9.** 73. **10.** 3, 7, 13, 37, since their product is 10, 101. **11.** Since $a = qb$ and $q = rc$ then $a = (rc)b = r(bc)$. **12.** $x = 5, y = -4$; $x = -8$, $y = 7$; $x = -21, y = 18$; $x = 18, y = -15$. **13.** $3x + 6y$ is divisible by 3 whenever x and y are integers, but 3 does not divide 22.

Chapter 10. Exer. 2 Page 168
1. (a) $3! + 1 = 7$ a prime, (b) $5! + 1 = 121 = 11^2$, (c) $7! + 1 = 5041 = 71^2$. **3.** (59, 61) (71, 73). **4.** (a) $40 = 3 + 37 = 11 + 29$, (b) $62 = 31 + 31 = 19 + 43$, (c) $84 = 41 + 43 = 5 + 79$, (d) $108 = 41 + 67 = 37 + 71$. **5.** For the divisors of 496 we have $1 + 2 + 4 + 8 + 16 + 31 + 62 + 124 + 248 + 496 = 992 = 2 \times 496$. **6.** $197 - 1 = 14^2$, $257 - 1 = 16^2$, $401 - 1 = 20^2$, $577 - 1 = 24^2$, $677 - 1 = 26^2$. **7.** $Q = n^2 - 1 = (n + 1)(n - 1)$ and if $n > 2$, this always gives a factorization of Q with neither factor equal to 1. **8.** $11 = 6^2 - 5^2$, $17 = 9^2 - 8^2$, $29 = 15^2 - 14^2$. For a composite number there will be more than one decomposition, for example $21 = 11^2 - 10^2 = 5^2 - 2^2$.

Chapter 10. Exer. 3 Page 170
1. (a) 25 (b) 113 (c) 36 (d) 1 (e) 101 (f) 2. **3.** If (1) D divides a, b, and c, and (2) if d divides a, b, and c implies d divides D, then we call D the greatest common divisor of a, b, and c. The g.c.d. of 48, 72, and 78 is 6. **4.** $(2n)^2 = 4n^2$. **5.** $(2n)^2 = 4n^2 \neq 4X + 2$ and $(2n + 1)^2 = 4n^2 + 4n + 1 = 4K + 1 \neq 4X + 2$.

Chapter 10. Exer. 4 Page 175
3. $100 + 576 = 676$. No. **4.** $t = 2, s = 1; \ t = 5, s = 4$.
5. $(1, 2, 3)$ and $(2, 2, 4)$. **6.** $x = z(z + 1)/2$ and
$y = z(z - 1)/2$ are both integers and give a solution to
$x^2 - y^2 = z^3$.

Chapter 11. Exer. 1 Page 180
1. 40. **2.** $28, 28^2 = 784$. **3.** $5^3 = 125, 50$. **4.** 2000.
5. 96. **6.** 315. **7.** 52. **8.** 105. **9.** $2^4 = 16$,
$4 \times 3 \times 3 = 36$. **10.** $2^{10} = 1024$.

Chapter 11. Exer. 2 Page 184
1. 10,10. **2.** 120,120. **3.** Yes. With each combination of k things selected, there is a combination of $(n - k)$
things left behind. Therefore $C(n, k) = C(n, n - k)$.
4. 720, 15,600. **5.** 720. **6.** 42, 7. **7.** 20, $C(n, 3) =$
$n(n - 1)(n - 2)/6$. **8.** $P(24, 3) = 12,144$, $24^3 = 13,824$.
9. $C(8, 4) = 70$, $C(8, 1) + C(8, 2) + C(8, 3) + C(8, 4) =$
162. **10.** $C(10, 3) = 120, C(n, 3)$. **11.** 126. **12.** 8.
13. 6. **14.** 11. **15.** 8. **16.** 20. **17.** 8. **18.** $n = 7$,
$k = 4$. **19.** $n = 15, k = 3$. **20.** $n = 3, k = 3; \ n = 4$,
$k = 4; \ n = 6, k = 5; \ n = 10, k = 6$.

Chapter 11. Exer. 3 Page 187
1. $2 \cdot 5! - 4 \cdot 4! = 144$. **2.** $2 \cdot 4! = 48$. **3.** $2(4!)^2 =$
1152. **4.** $P(7, 4) = 840$. **5.** $P(6, 3) = 120$. **6.** (a) 3360,
(b) 60, (c) 630, (d) 3780, (e) 34,650. **7.** $C(6, 1) +$
$C(6, 2) + C(6, 3) + C(6, 4) + C(6, 5) + C(6, 6) = 63$.
8. 103,776. **9.** 9. **10.** 3, $(n - 1)!/2$. **11.** $C(8, 4) \times$
$3 \times 3/2 = 315$. **12.** $7 \times 5 \times 3 \times 1 = 105$, $105 \times 2^4 =$
1680. **13.** $p(p - 1)q(q - 1)/4$. **14.** $C(n, 4)$.
15. $3C(n, 4)$. **16.** $C(n, 2) - C(k, 2) + 1$.
17. $C(p + 2, 2) \ C(q + 2, 2)$.

Chapter 12. Geometry, Page 192
1. True. If the sides of the triangle have lengths a, b, and c
select as radii $(-a + b + c)/2$, $(a - b + c)/2$, and
$(a + b - c)/2$. **2.** False. In the limit case where two
of the vertices coincide three of the triangles have zero
area. **3.** True. Let b_1 and b_2 be the bases of the triangles
of area A_1 and A_2 respectively. Then

$$\frac{A_1}{A_2} = \frac{b_1}{b_2} = \frac{A_4}{A_3}$$

and hence $A_1 A_3 = A_2 A_4$. **4.** True. **5.** True. The proof requires analytic geometry and is a little difficult. **6.** False. The proof is difficult. **7.** True. This is known as Morley's Theorem and the proof is very difficult. **8.** False. Let the points A, D, and C lie on a straight line and observe that D may be any point between A and C. **9.** True. In fact there are always two solid colored triangles.[1] D_1. **10.** T. D_1. **11.** F. In fact the equilateral triangle has the smallest area. D_1. **12.** T. **13.** T. D_2. **14.** F. If we select lines that lie in three parallel planes, the minimizing figure may be a degenerate triangle with collinear vertices. **15.** T. **16.** T. This follows from problem 15. **17.** F. For an equilateral triangle of side 10 we have $P = 30$ and $4\sqrt{3}\,A = 300$. **18.** T. D_3. **19.** T. D_3. **2).** T. D_3. **21.** F. Consider a circle and a concentric ring domain as shown in Figure B. **22.** T. D_3. **23.** T.

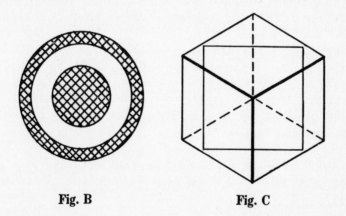

Fig. B   **Fig. C**

D_2. Consider the points that are the vertices of a regular pentagon plus the center of the circumscribed circle. **24.** T. D_2. **25.** T. D_1. **26.** F. There are four such

---

[1]Henceforth we use the symbols D_1, D_2, D_3, to indicate that the proof is somewhat difficult, difficult, and very difficult.

diagonals. **27.** T. D_2. Figure C shows a cube as viewed along a main diagonal and a possible location for cutting the hole.

Chapter 12. Algebra, Page 197

1. F. $x^2 + 1 = 0$ has no real roots. **2.** T. D_3. This was first proved by Gauss. **3.** F. The polynomial $x^2 - 4x + 4 = 0$ has only the single root $x = 2$. **4.** T. D_1. **5.** T. D_1. **6.** T. D_1. **7.** F. D_2. **8.** F. D_2. **9.** T. $\sqrt{2} + \sqrt{3}$ is a root of $x^4 - 10x^2 + 1 = 0$. **10.** T. D_1. **11.** $D = (x - 2)(x - 3)(x - 4) \cdots (x - n)$. **12.** F. This determinant is zero for all values of x, y, z and w. **13.** T. D_2. This is known as the Gauss Lemma. **14.** T. D_3. **15.** (*a*) T. D_2. (*b*) T. D_2.

Chapter 12. Sequences and series, Page 200

1. Con. Limit is 0. **2.** Div. **3.** Con. Limit is 0. **4.** Con. Limit is 0. **5.** Con. Limit is 2. **6.** Con. D_2. (see problem 15 of the algebra set). The limit is not among the numbers we have previously studied. It is approximately 2.71828 and is denoted by the letter *e*. **7.** Div. **8.** Con. The sum is $\frac{3}{2}$. **9.** Div. **10.** Con. D_2. The sum is 2. **11.** Div. D_1. **12.** Con. The sum is $\frac{10}{9}$. **13.** T. D_2. First proved by Leibniz. **14.** T. It is not difficult to show that this series is equal to the one of problem 13. **15.** T. D_2. If L is the limit it must satisfy the equation $L = 1/(2 + L)$ and this equation has only one positive root, $\sqrt{2} - 1$.

Chapter 12. Number Theory, Page 204

1. T . To obtain $(2k + 1)^2$ set $n = k(k + 1)/2$. **2.** T. D_3. **3.** F. Set $n = 34$. Then $10n + 3 = 343 = 7^3$. Also if $n = -3$ then $10n - 3 = -27 = (-3)^3$. **4.** F. If $n = 5$, $4 \times 5 + 1 = 21 \neq a^2 + b^2$. **5.** T. D_1. **6.** T. D_3. **7.** T. **8.** T. Use the result of problem 7; set $X = a^2 + b^2$ and $Y = c^2 + d^2$. **9.** F. If $n = 3^5 \times 5 \times 7 = 8,505$, then the sum of its divisors is 17,472 and this is larger than $2 \times 8,505 = 17,010$. **10.** T. If $N = 2^3 \times 3^4 = 648$, then $\frac{N}{2} = 324 = 18^2$ and $\frac{N}{3} = 216 = 6^3$. **11.** T.

$n(n+1)(n+2)(n+3) + 1 = n^4 + 6n^3 + 11n^2 + 6n + 1 = (n^2 + 3n + 1)^2.$ **12.** T. $M = 2^{15} \times 3^{10} \times 5^6 = 30{,}233{,}088{,}000{,}000$ is the smallest such integer.   **13.** T. D_2.

14. F.   There are two others $\dfrac{19}{95} = \dfrac{1}{5}$ and $\dfrac{16}{64} = \dfrac{1}{4}$.

15. T. D_2.

BIBLIOGRAPHY

The titles listed below include all of those referred to in this book. We have marked with a star (✦) those that should be in the library of every high school in the country.

✦1. W. W. R. Ball, *Mathematical Recreations and Essays,* 6th ed. (New York: The Macmillan Co., 1914).

2. W. W. R. Ball, *A Short Account of the History of Mathematics,* 4th ed. (New York: The Macmillan Co., 1908).

✦3. E. T. Bell, *Men of Mathematics* (New York: Simon & Schuster, 1937).

4. Samuel Borofsky, *Elementary Theory of Equations* (New York: The Macmillan Co., 1950).

5. Florian Cajori, *A History of Mathematics,* 2nd ed. (New York: The Macmillan Co., 1919).

✦6. Richard Courant and Herbert Robbins, *What Is Mathematics?* (London: Oxford University Press, 1941).

✦7. Arnold Dresden, *An Invitation to Mathematics* (New York: Henry Holt and Company, 1936).

✦8. Howard Eves, *An Introduction to the History of Mathematics* (New York: Rinehart and Co., Inc., 1953).

9. L. I. Golovina and I. M. Yaglom, *Mathematical Induction in Geometry* (Boston: D. C. Heath and Co., 1961).

10. A. W. Goodman, *Plane Trigonometry* (New York: John Wiley and Sons, Inc., 1959).

11. Robert Jungk, *Brighter Than a Thousand Suns* (New York: Harcourt Brace and Co., 1958).

✦12. Maurice Kraitchik, *Mathematical Recreations* (New York: Dover Publications, Inc., 1953).

✦13. Edmund Landau, *Foundations of Analysis* (New York: Chelsea Publishing Co., 1951).

14. Lillian R. Lieber and Hugh Gray Lieber, *Galois and the Theory of Groups* (Lancaster, Pa.: The Science Press Printing Co., 1932).

✦15. Lillian R. Lieber and Hugh Gray Lieber, *Non-Euclidean Geometry* (New York: Academy Press, 1931); 2nd edition (Lancaster, Pa.: The Science Press Printing Co., 1940).

✦16. Lillian R. Lieber and Hugh Gray Lieber, *The Education of T. C. Mits* (New York: W. W. Norton & Co., 1944).

17. Lillian R. Lieber and Hugh Gray Lieber, *The Einstein Theory of Relativity* (New York: Rinehart and Co., Inc., 1945).

✦18. Lillian R. Lieber and Hugh Gray Lieber, *Modern Mathematics for T. C. Mits* (London: George Allen and Unwin Ltd., 1946).

✦19. Lillian R. Lieber and Hugh Gray Lieber, *Take A Number: Mathematics for the Two Billion* (Tempe, Ariz.: Jacques Cattell Press, 1946).

✦20. Lillian R. Lieber and Hugh Gray Lieber, *Mits, Wits, and Logic* (New York: W. W. Norton & Co., 1947); Revised edition (New York: Galois Press, 1954).

✦21. Lillian R. Lieber and Hugh Gray Lieber, *Infinity* (New York: Rinehart and Co., Inc., 1953).

22. C. E. Love, *Elements of Analytic Geometry* (New York: The Macmillan Co., 1950).

23. I. Niven and H. Zuckerman, *An Introduction to the Theory of Numbers* (New York: John Wiley and Sons, Inc., 1960).

✦24. G. Polya, *Mathematics and Plausible Reasoning* (Princeton, N. J.: Princeton University Press, 1954).

✦25. G. Polya, *Patterns of Plausible Inference* (Princeton, N. J.: Princeton University Press, 1954).

✦26. Hans Rademacher and Otto Toeplitz, *The Enjoyment of Mathematics* (Princeton, N. J.: Princeton University Press, 1957).

27. Vera Sanford, *A Short History of Mathematics* (New York: Houghton Mifflin Co., 1930).

28. Smith, Salkover and Justice, *Analytic Geometry* (John Wiley and Sons, 1954).

✦29. Hugo Steinhaus, *Mathematical Snapshots* (New York: Oxford University Press, 1951).

30. B. M. Stewart, *Theory of Numbers* (New York: The Macmillan Co., 1952).

Index

221